TOTAL GUITAR

MAKING YOU A BETTER GUITARIST

6 CLASSIC TRACKS

I AM THE RESURRECTION

THE STONE ROSES

Plus...five more classic hit songs

Wise Publications
London/ New York/ Sydney/ Paris/ Copenhagen/ Madrid
www.internetmusicshop.com

Exclusive Distributors:
Music Sales Limited
8/9 Frith Street, London W1V 5TZ, England.

Music Sales Pty Limited
120 Rothschild Avenue, Rosebery, NSW 2018, Australia.

Order No. AM956461
ISBN 0-7119-7464-0
This book © Copyright 1999 by Wise Publications

Cover and Book Design By Nicholas Ellis
Music Engraving by Digital Music Art

Photographs courtesy of Redferns, London Features International and Rex Features.
Printed in the United Kingdom by Caligraving Limited, Thetford, Norfolk.

Your Guarantee of Quality
As publishers, we strive to produce every book to the highest standards. This book has been carefully designed to minimise
awkward page turns and to make playing from it a real pleasure.
Particular care has been given to specifying acid-free, neutral-sized paper made from pulps which have not been elemental
chlorine bleached. This pulp is from farmed sustainable forests and was produced with special regard for the environment. The
printing and binding have been planned to ensure a sturdy, attractive publication which should give years of enjoyment.
If your copy fails to meet our high standards, please inform us and we will gladly replace it.

Music Sales' complete catalogue describes thousands of titles and is available in full colour by subject, direct from Music Sales
Limited. Please state your areas of interest and send a cheque/ postal order for £1.50 for postage to: Music Sales Limited,
Newmarket Road, Bury St. Edmunds, Suffolk IP33 3YB.

www.internetmusicshop.com

The Low E is tuned down to a D

Love Spreads - The Stone Roses

```
Intro
E|----------------------------------------------------------------------
B|----------------------------------------------------------------------
G|----------------------------------------------------------------------
d|----------------------------------------------------------------------
A|-------5-----5/8---5/8---5/8--5-------0---3-5---5/10---8---5---0-5------
D|-0---------0----------------------0------------------------------0--
```

```
--------------------------------------------------------------------------
--------------------------------------------------------------------------
----7-----------------------------------------7---------------------------
--7---7\---------------------------0---0-------0--------------------------
---------0-5/8---5/8---5/8-----3---5/8-----------0-3---5--8---5-8---5----
--------------------------------------------------------------------------
```

```
--------------------------------------------------------------------------
-----------------------------------------------------------10-----8---
--7-----------------------------------------------------9------7---
--7-----------------------------0-------5---5\--0--/5--/6--/7----/7-7--/5-5---
------0---5/8---5/8--5/8--------------------------------------------------
--------------------------------0----------------------------------------
```

```
                                            Verse
----------------------------------------||---------------------------------
8---------------------------------------||---------------------------------
7-----------7---------------------------||*--------------------------------
5-----------7---------------------------||*--------------------------3---3h5p3--
----5/8---5-----0---3---5---8---5-8---||--5---0-3-5-0-5---0-3-5-----------
----------------------------------------||---------------------------------
```

```
----------------------------------------------------------------------------
----------------------------------------------------------------------------
----------------------------------------------------------------------------
p0------------------5-7p5p0-5p3p0---------------------3---3h5p3p0-----
---5---0-3-5-0-5---5-8--------------5---0-3-5-0-5---0-3-5------------5---
----------------------------------------------------------------------------
```

```
----------------------------------------------------------------------------
----------------------------------------------------------------------------
----------------------------------------------------------------------------
-----------------------------------------------3---3h5p3p0-------------
--0-3-5-0-5---3-5-3-0-3-0---------3-5-0-5---0-3-5------------5---0-3-5----
--------------------------5-0-0--------------------------------------------
```

```
--------------------------------------------------------------------
--------------------------------------------------------------------
--------------------------------------------------------------------
```

```
----------5-7p5p0-5p3p0----------------------3---3h5p3p0-----------------
0-5---5-8---------------5---0-3-5-0-5---0-3-5-----------5---0-3-5-0-5----
------------------------------------------------------------------------
                .
------------------------------------------------------------------------


------------------------------------------------------------------------
------------------------------------------------------------------------
------------------------------------------------------------5-----------
------3=----3---3-5-5-5-5-5-5-5---5-5-5-5-3-------5-5-5-3---5/7---7-5-3h5--
--5-------5---5-----------------------------5-3----------5---------------
------------------------------------------------------------------------


------------------------------------------------------------------------
------------------------------------------------------------------------
------------------------------------------------------------------------
p3-----------------------------3---3h5p3---------------------------------
---5-3---3-5---3-5---5---0-3-5-----------5-3---3-5-----3-5------3-5---3-----
-----------0-----0----------------------------0------0------------------
------------------------------------------------------------------------


------------------------------------------------------------------------
------------------------------------------------------------------------
------------------------------------------------5/7-5-----------
----3-----3---3-5-5-5-5-5-5-5---5-5-5-5-3-------5-5-5-3---------7-5-3h5p3--
5-------5---5------------------------5-3----------5------------------
------------------------------------------------------------------------


------------------------------------------------------------------------
------------------------------------------------------------------------
------------------------------------------------------------------------
--------------------------------------------------------------5^W---
-5-3---3-5-----3-5---5---0-3-5---5h8p5-3-0-3-5-5-5-3-5-0-5-----3-0---------
----------0------0------------------------------------------------------
------------------------------------------------------------------------


------------------------------------------------------------------------
------------------------------------------------------------------------
-------------------------------5------------------------------------
--5^W--5-3---------5^W---5^W---3-5^W---5-3-3h5p3-------------3------------
----------5p3p0-------------------------5-3-5---5-5---5--3-5-----
------------------------------------------------------------------------


--------------------------||
--------------------------||
-------------------------*||
---------------7p5p0-5p3p0-*||
5-5---5-0-3-5--------------||
--------------------------||
```

Introduction by Harry Wylie   **4**

A Design For Life *(Manic Street Preachers)*   **5**

Don't Look Back In Anger *(Oasis)*   **12**

Hush *(Kula Shaker)*   **43**

I Am The Resurrection *(The Stone Roses)*   **26**

Walk This Way *(Aerosmith)*   **52**

Where The Streets Have No Name *(U2)*   **61**

Notation and Tablature   **79**

CD Track Listing   **80**

Hello, I'm Harry Wylie, the editor of Total Guitar, the country's best-selling and most popular guitar magazine. Welcome to a brand new series of music books which are based on TG's hugely popular Classic Track series.

Over the past five years, my magazine has featured one classic guitar song per issue in all its glorious detail, for readers to learn, play and jam with over a CD backing track. Only the most requested guitar moments have been chosen, featuring some of the most famous guitarists and artists in the world - from Hendrix to Clapton, The Stone Roses to The Beatles and Dire Straits to the Manic Street Preachers - and six of them are featured in this book.

This exciting new series from Music Sales brings you the highlights of the last five years of Total Guitar - I really hope you enjoy them! And if you do, why not pick up a copy of Total Guitar every month... Be seeing you!

How to use the CD

On the TG CD you'll find demonstration versions and backing tracks of each of the six songs in this book. Listen to the audio in conjunction with the music and TAB in the book, and you'll soon be playing along! If you're not sure how to read TAB, check out our one-page guide at the back of this book.

Sometimes the demo version is split up across several tracks to let you skip straight to the section you're interested in - refer to the verse and chorus markings in the music to identify each section.

Timing boxes are given for each transcription to help you find your way around - these always refer to the backing track, and may not always match up with the demonstration versions.

This Enhanced CD can be played on your hi-fi or on your multimedia PC. If you are on the Internet and want to browse the World's largest selection of sheet music, simply place the CD in your CD-Rom drive and follow the on-screen instructions. **TG**

Further reading ...

If you're a fan of TG Classic Tracks, then why not check out some of the other book and CD titles available from Music Sales.

The 'Play Guitar With ...' series is the biggest range of CD books for guitarists currently available - allowing you to play along with more than 30 of the world's most famous bands and artists.

Each book contains full TAB, standard notation, lyrics and chord symbols, plus a specially recorded CD containing full demonstration versions of each track, and professional 'soundalike' backing tracks.

Here's a small selection of the titles available:

AC/DC
Order No. AM955900

the kinks
Order No. AM951863

the beatles
Order No. NO90665

kula shaker
Order No. AM943767

the beatles Book 2
Order No. NO90667

john lennon
Order No. AM943756

blur
Order No. AM935320

bob marley
Order No. AM937739

bon jovi
Order No. AM92558

metallica
Order No. AM92559

eric clapton
Order No. AM950862

alanis morissette
Order No. AM943723

phil collins
Order No. AM928147

oasis
Order No. AM943712

the cranberries
Order No. AM941699

elvis presley
Order No. AM937090

dire straits
Order No. DG70735

pulp
Order No. AM938124

david gilmour
Order No.AM954602

sting
Order No. AM928092

buddy holly
Order No. AM943734

the stone roses
Order No. AM943701

john lee hooker
Order No. AM951885

the stone roses Book 2
Order No. AM955890

b.b. king
Order No. AM951874

paul weller
Order No. AM937827

All these titles are available from your local music shop, and can also be ordered over the internet by visiting the Music Sales website at www.internetmusicshop.com.

Fretboxes

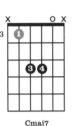

Cmaj7

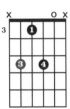

Dm13

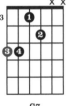

G7

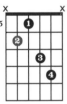

Ebmaj7

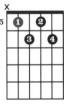

Dm7b5

Shown here are all the shapes you need to play the arpeggiated chords which are used in the verse – note that all of these should have the sixth string detuned a whole tone to D.

A Design For Life
MANIC STREET PREACHERS

Learn to play this modern guitar classic, which is fast overtaking Stairway To Heaven and Smoke On The Water as _the_ practice booth favourite in your local music store.

James Dean Bradfield - Libraries gave him power

EVERY guitarist wants to write a music shop classic – one of those songs that everyone plays as they try out that new Les Paul they could never afford. Well move aside *Smoke On The Water* and *Stairway...* – in the last two years I've heard this song more than any other in that barometer of style, the practice booth.

Apart from the arpeggios on the intro, which have to be picked cleanly and accurately (and contain some nasty stretches), the rest of the song is fairly straightforward. On the original recording there are at least two guitars – one in dropped D and one in normal tuning – and our transcription features the most important points of each.

For the guitar sound, it's not essential that you play a Gibson Les Paul as James Dean Bradfield does, but do try to get a bright and fairly thick tone. The distortion or overdrive should be switched in for the "we don't talk about love" bridge section, and off again at the end of each chorus. **TG**

A Design For Life
Music by James Dean Bradfield & Sean Moore
Lyrics by Nicky Wire

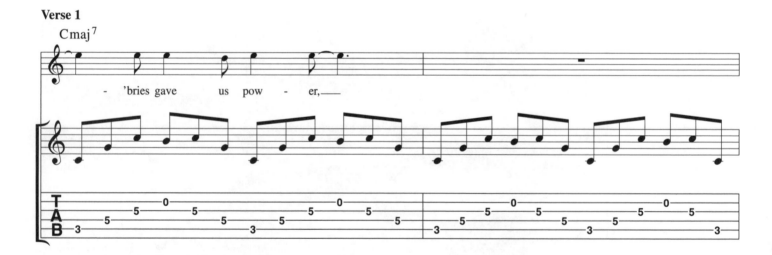

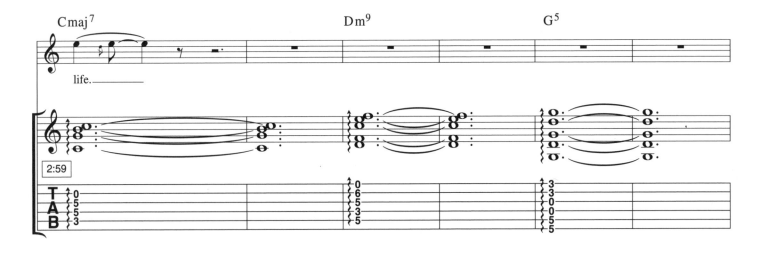

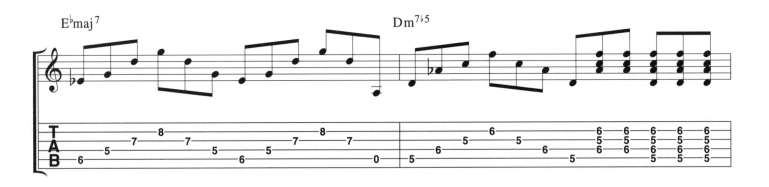

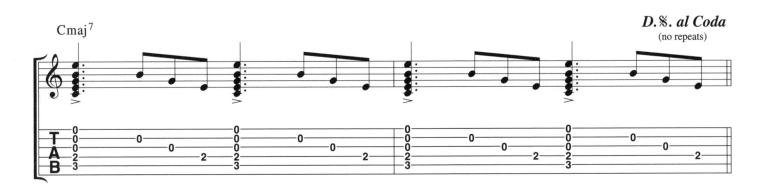

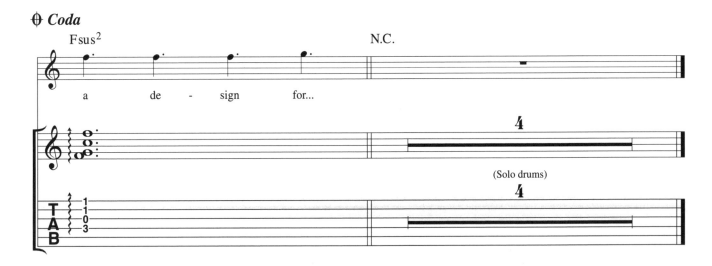

Don't Look Back In Anger
OASIS

Fretboxes

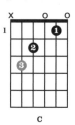

C

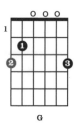

G

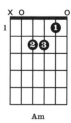

Am

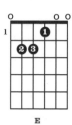

E

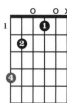

E/G# (G#dim)

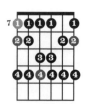

C major scale

Shown here are the open chords used by Noel. Use the C major scale to work out the vocal melody.

This 1995 track from What's The Story (Morning Glory) was one of the most up-to-date songs ever to be printed as a classic track in Total Guitar, and it's easy to see why!

Noel Gallagher, pictured with one of his favoured guitars, an Epiphone Riviera.

CLASSIC tracks often take many years to make it to these pages. Like fine wine they have to mature, until they're an integral part of guitar-playing culture. The Oasis phenomenon is a rare exception – this is the most contemporary transcription we've ever done, and the song has easily achieved the status of 'modern classic'.

TECHNIQUE & SOUND

One possible reason for Noel Gallagher's success, both as a songwriter and a guitarist, is that he uses the major pentatonic and major scales, creating a more melodic feel than the blues-based approach of some rock players. The melody from *Don't Look Back In Anger* uses simple major scale fragments, and the solo is almost entirely major pentatonic – he also favours this scale in other solos, including *Some Might Say* (which in itself is influenced by George Harrison's solo from *Let It Be*). Noel uses all three positions of C major pentatonic in the song's guitar solo. To vary the rhythms, he throws in hammer-ons, pull-offs

and bends, usually using whole-tone (two fret) intervals.

Although Noel has used Strats – in fact *Don't Look Back In Anger* was recorded with one – he's fondest of humbucking guitars, usually Epiphone Rivieras, and more recently his Supernova signature model. Rhythm parts use heavy overdrive through various amps, but solos almost always use a Marshall head "to give it a bit of bollocks," as he puts it.

TOTAL RIP-OFF?

Oasis are renowned for 'borrowing' tunes from other songs, but surely the *Imagine*-style intro takes the biscuit. What do you have to say for yourself Noel? "I suppose fifty percent of that is there to wind people up. And the other fifty percent is saying, 'this is how songs come about – they're inspired by songs like *Imagine*'. So some 13 year old kid might hear that then go and buy the album. D'you know what I mean?" **TG**

Don't Look Back In Anger

Words & Music by Noel Gallagher

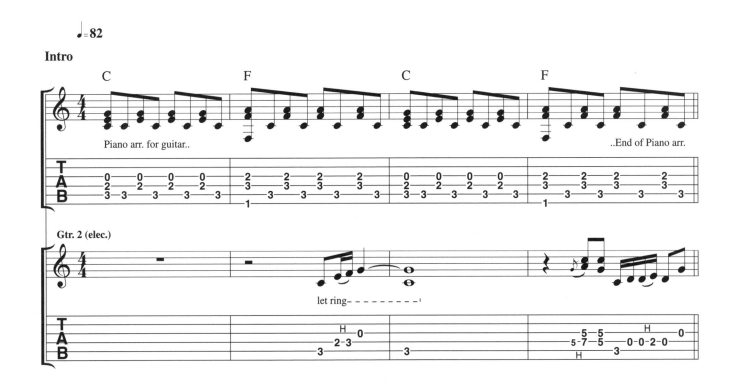

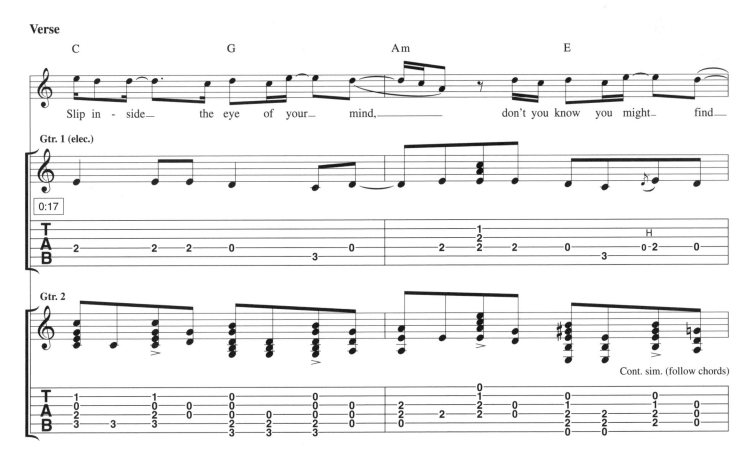

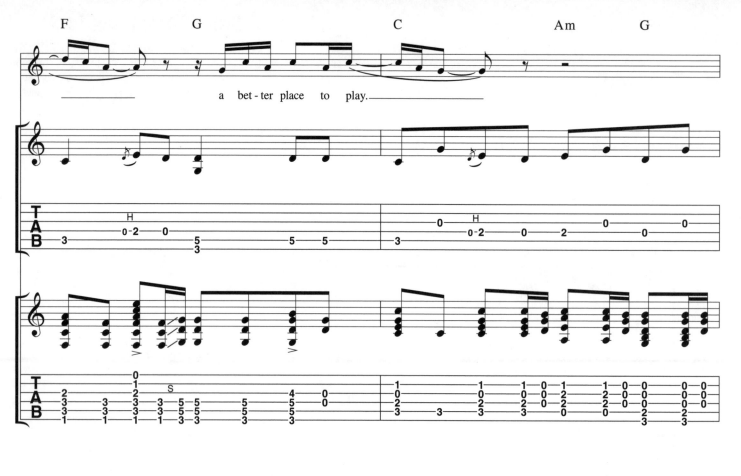

a bet - ter place to play.

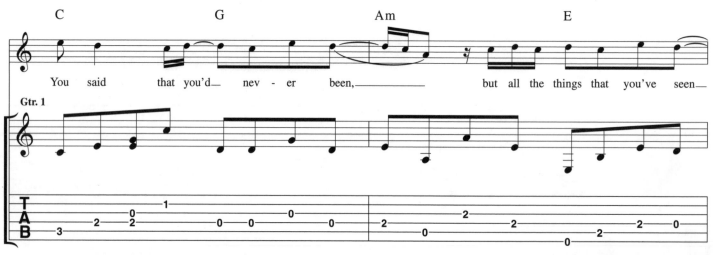

C   G   Am   E

You said that you'd— nev - er been,_____ but all the things that you've seen—

Gtr. 1

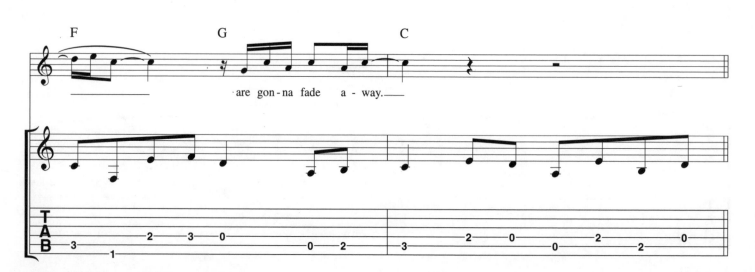

are gon - na fade a - way.—

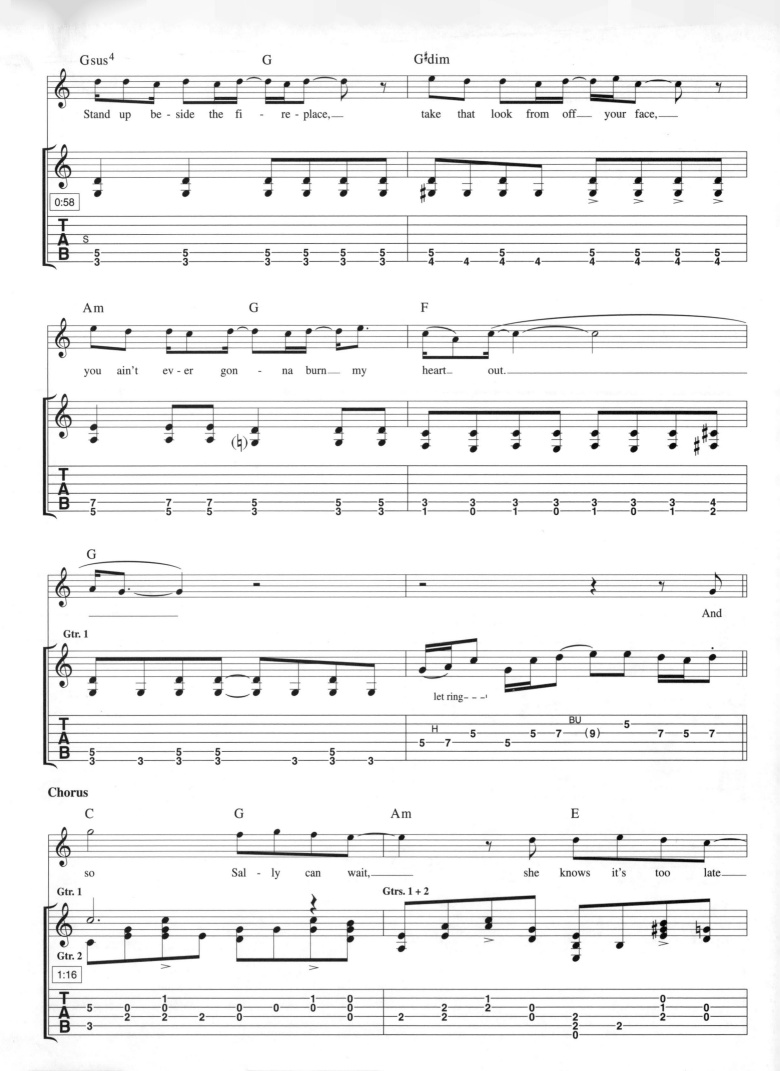

Bridge

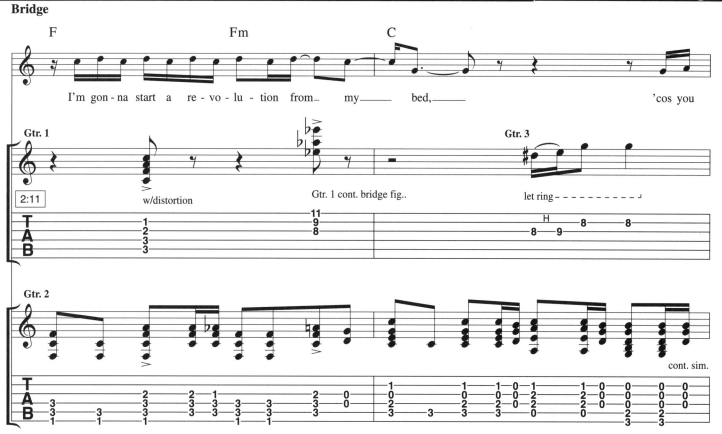

F — Fm — C

I'm gon-na start a re-vo-lu-tion from my bed, 'cos you

Gtr. 1

2:11   w/distortion   Gtr. 1 cont. bridge fig..   Gtr. 3   let ring

Gtr. 2   cont. sim.

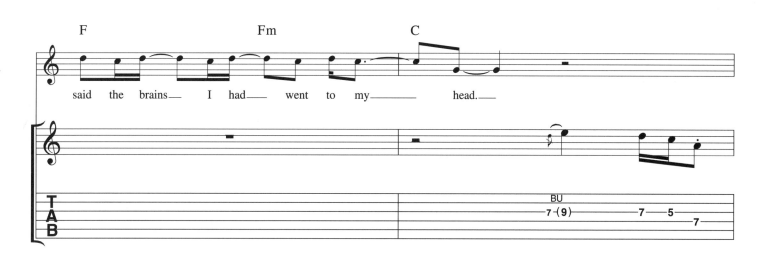

F — Fm — C

said the brains I had went to my head.

BU

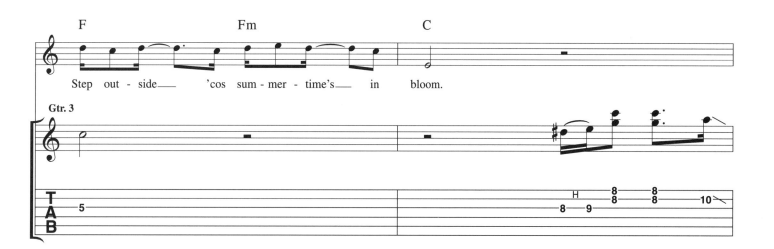

F — Fm — C

Step out-side 'cos sum-mer-time's in bloom.

Gtr. 3

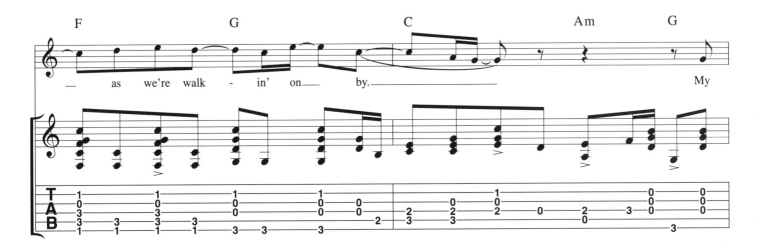

as we're walk - in' on — by. _____ My

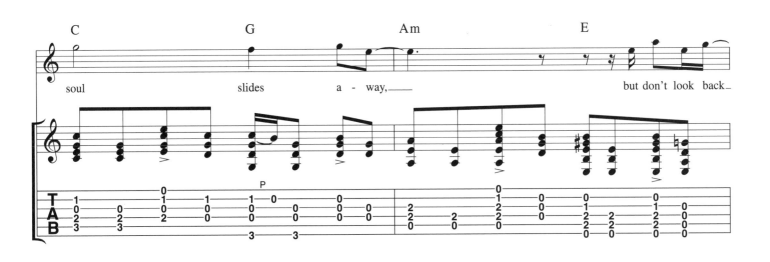

soul   slides   a - way, ____   but don't look back__

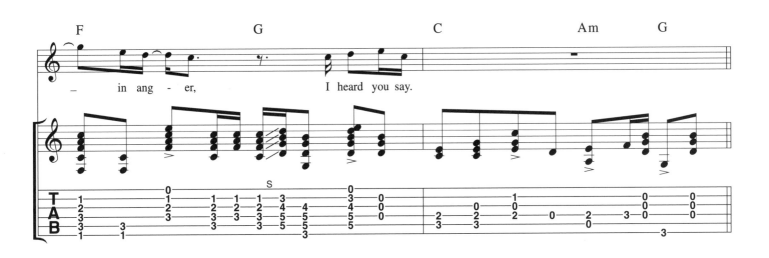

— in ang - er,   I heard you say.

Solo

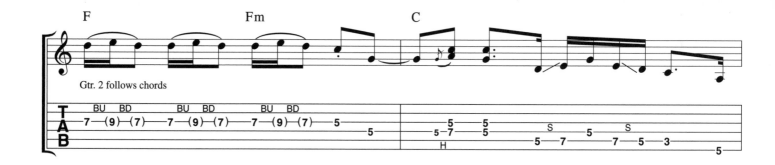

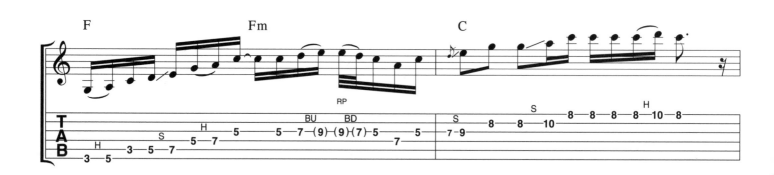

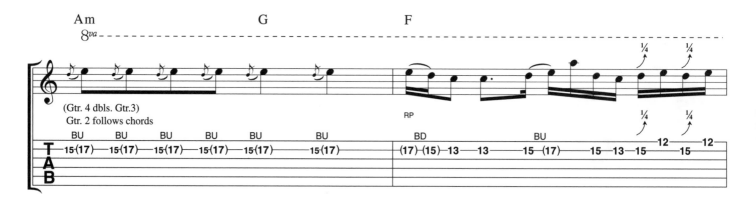

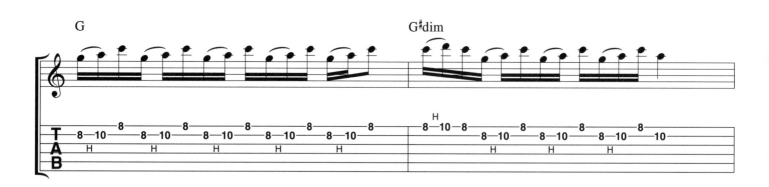

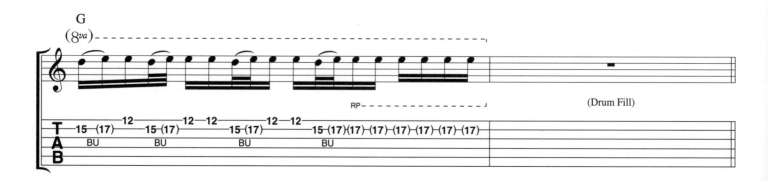

Chorus

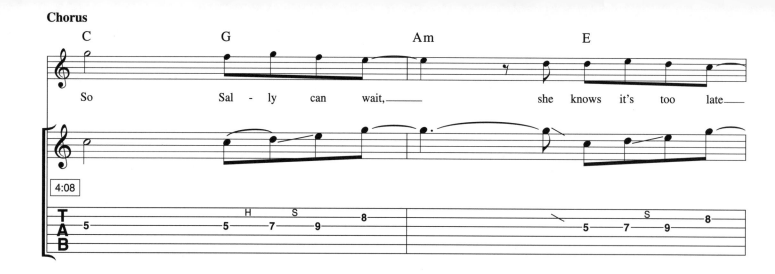

So Sal - ly can wait,_____ she knows it's too late_____

`4:08`

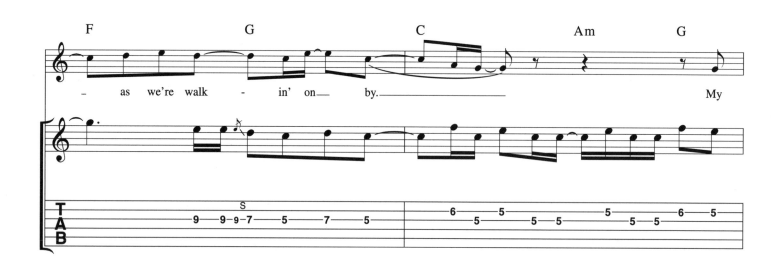

— as we're walk - in' on— by._____ My

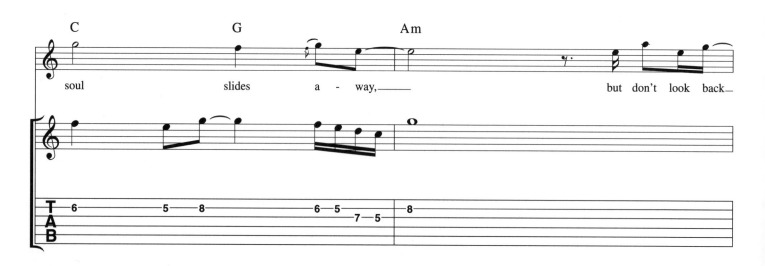

soul slides a - way,_____ but don't look back—

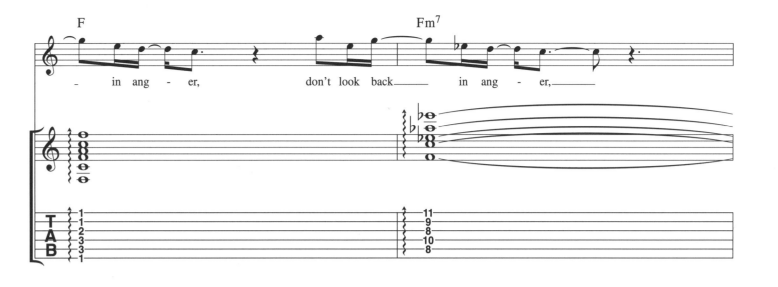

F   Fm⁷

_ in ang - er,   don't look back___ in ang - er,___

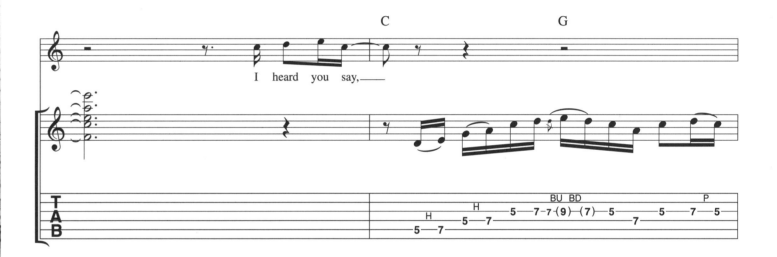

C   G

I heard you say,___

Am   E   F   Fm   C

at least not to - day.___

On the CD

TRACK 5
Full performance

TRACK 6
Backing track only

Fretboxes

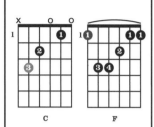

C   F

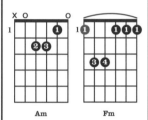

Am   Fm

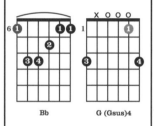

Bb   G (Gsus)4

Cm pentatonic

Shown here are novice-friendly versions of the song's chords, which can be strummed throughout.

If you fancy having a go at improvising your own solo over the outro, then start with the Cm pentatonic scale, which which is given above. Although Squire's soloing sometimes strays into other positions, the bulk of the outro solo is based on this scale shape.

Note: your guitar should be tuned down a semitone to match the original, which is in the key of B.

I Am The Resurrection

THE STONE ROSES

This 1989 album track featured John Squire in fearsome soloing mode. Learn to play along with our full eight minute transcription!

John Squire - The New Jimmy Page?

THERE are at least five versions of this track available. Usually, with Classic Tracks, we transcribe the single version of songs, but with this eight-minute epic (not to mention three-minute guitar solo) there was no alternative – we had to transcribe the whole thing.

TECHNIQUE

The entire first verse doesn't have any guitar on it at all – we've arranged the bass guitar part for six-string electric so you've got something to play over this section. But after the guitar enters (just before the bridge) it's pretty much lead playing all the way – even the arpeggiated chords are more like bass-end solos in places. But it's not until the

outro that Squire really lets rip. He's usually reticent about discussing his days with the Roses, but even so, he's pleased with I Am The Resurrection;

"I like the fortuitous ending… we had some bits left over on tape which we just dropped in at exactly the right point – that little rhythm guitar bit at the end. I think we only tried it once, so it's a bit out of time. I like it, though."

The solo itself is typically Squire, with its high-speed loose pentatonic feel and Zep-influenced phrasing, though it's worth noting that he's a considerably more advanced player these days (check out his playing on Second Coming and The Seahorses' Do It Yourself) – it's nice to see that even the best can improve! **TG**

I Am The Resurrection
Words & Music by John Squire & Ian Brown

♩=132

Intro

(8 bars drumkit)

Bass arr. for gtr.

0:18

Verse 1

0:21

Down down,   you   bring me   down.—   I   hear you   knock-

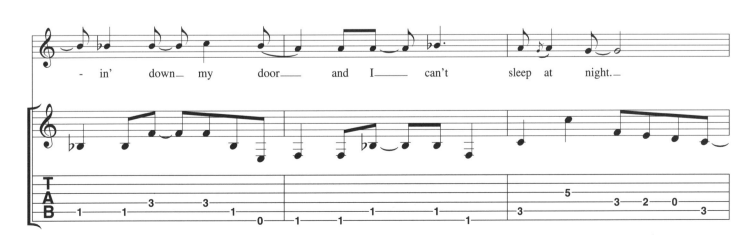

- in' down— my   door——   and I——   can't   sleep   at   night.—

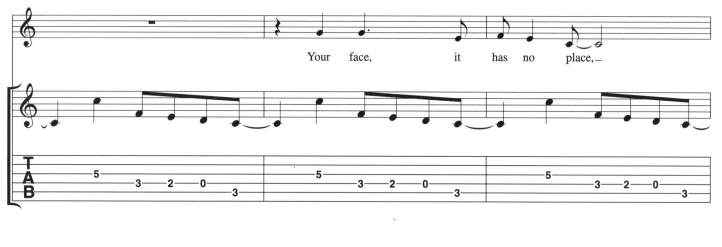

Your face,   it has no place,—

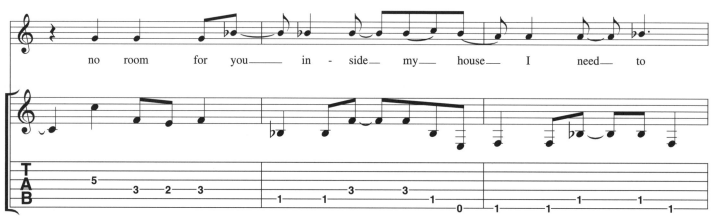

no room   for you——   in - side—   my—   house—   I   need—   to

be   a - lone.——

(Bass arr. ends)   Gtr w/heavy dist.

Bridge

Am

Don't   waste   your   words,   I   don't   need   an - y - thing—   from   you.—

F

0:46
1:27

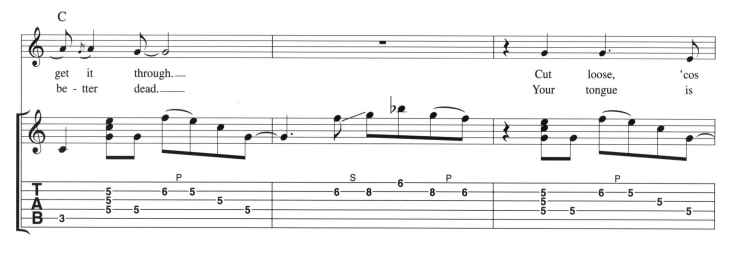

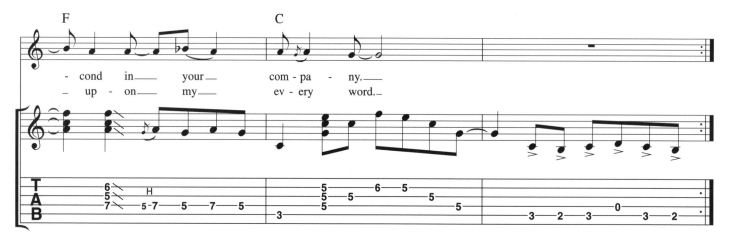

Bridge

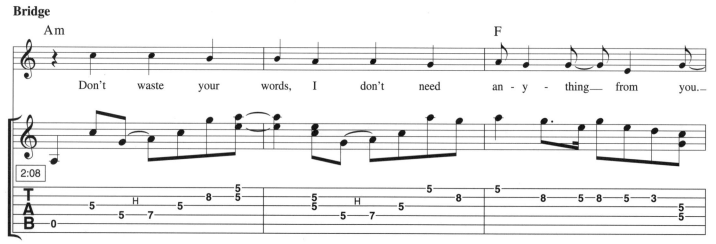

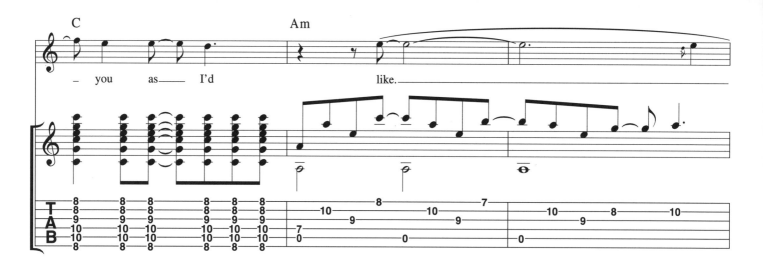

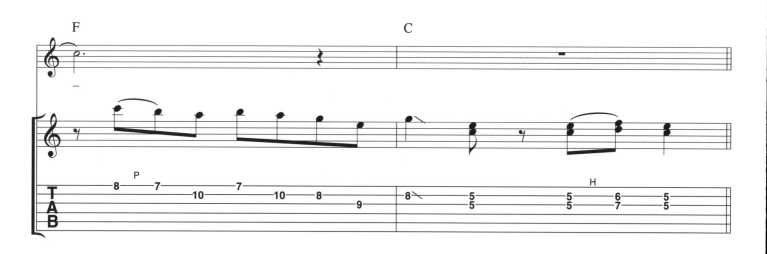

1st Guitar Solo

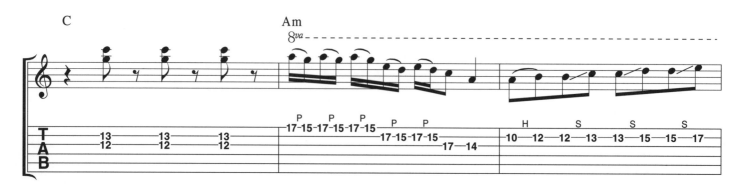

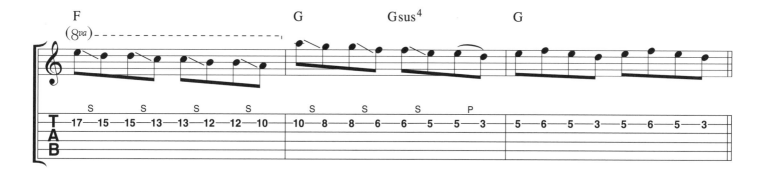

Chorus

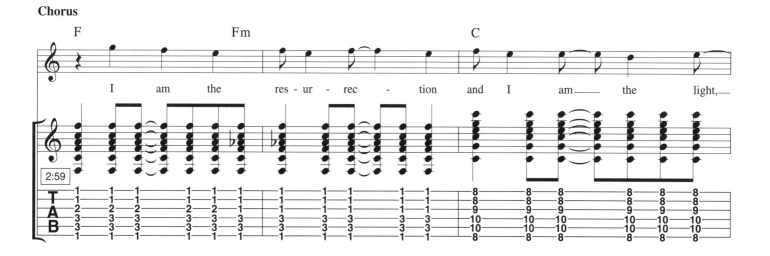

I am the res - ur - rec - tion and I am ___ the light, ___

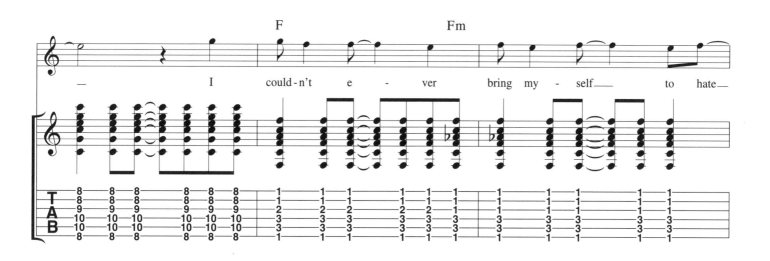

___ I could-n't e - ver bring my-self ___ to hate ___

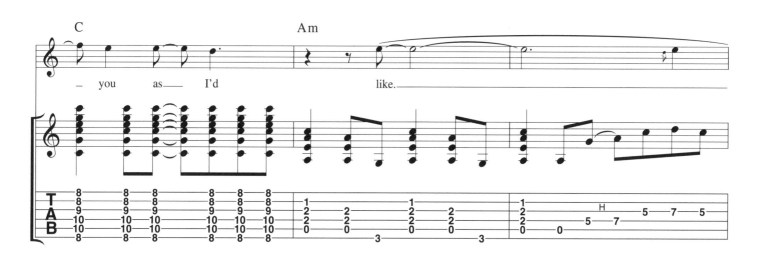

_ you as ___ I'd like. ___

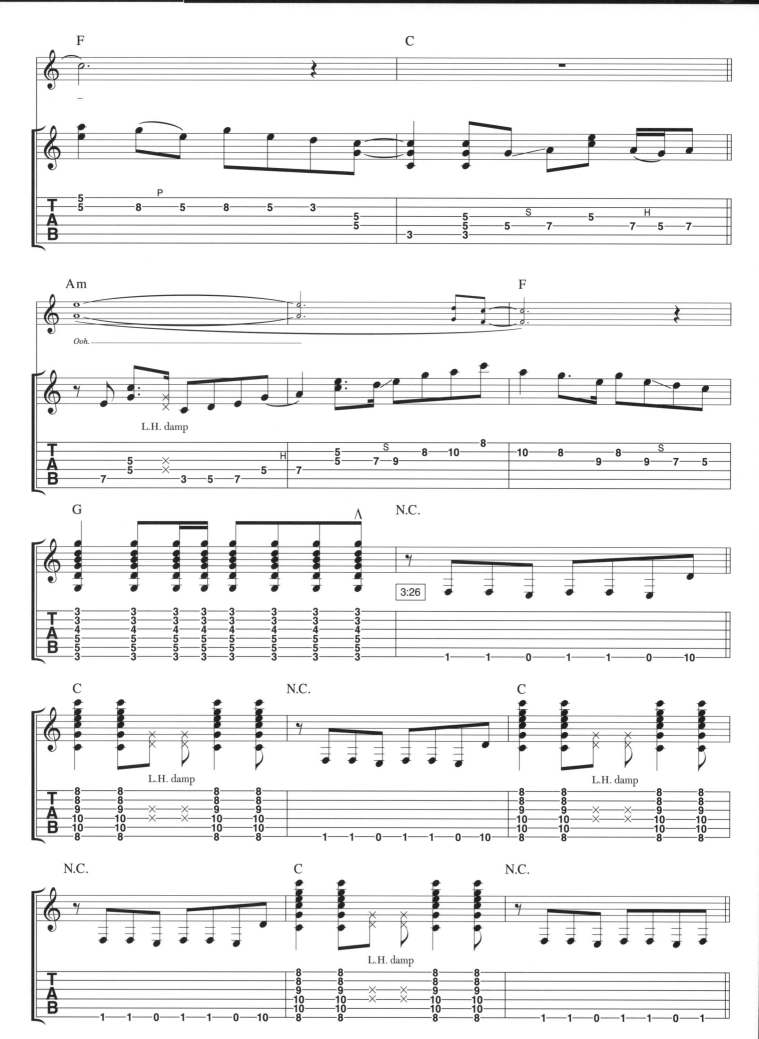

2nd Guitar Solo

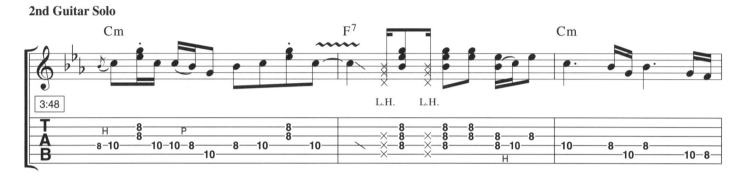

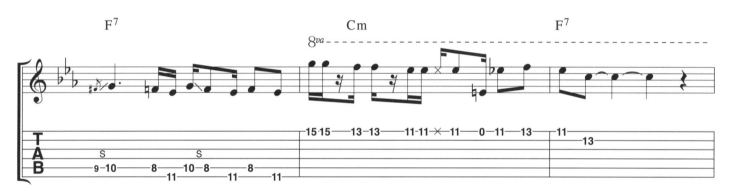

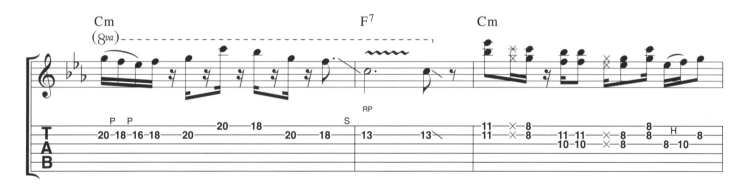

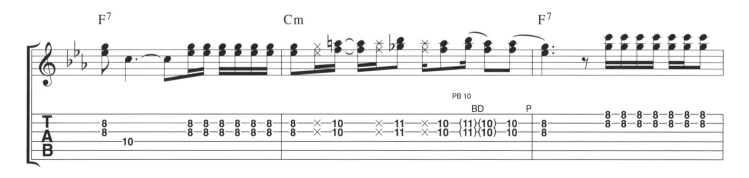

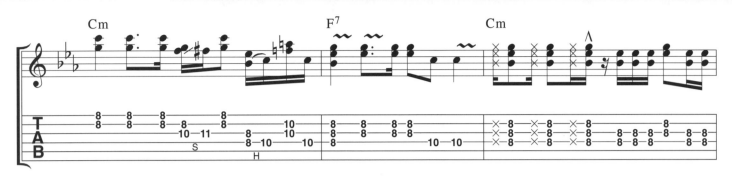

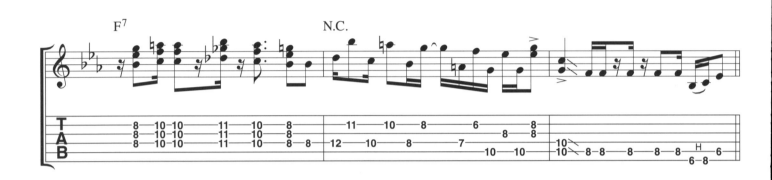

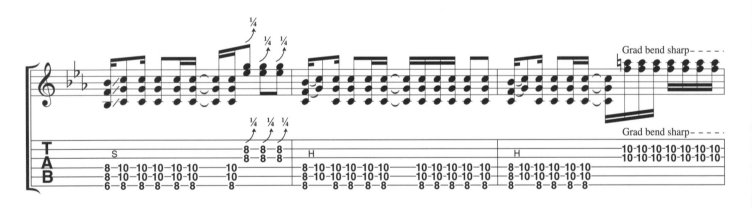

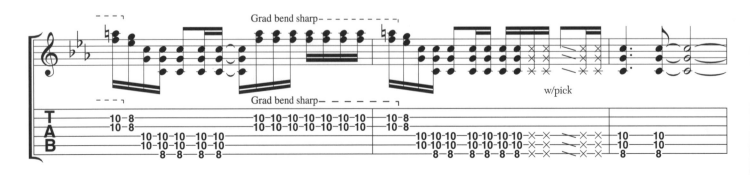

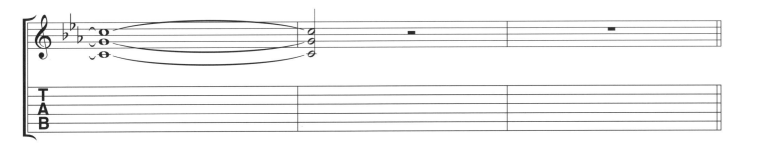

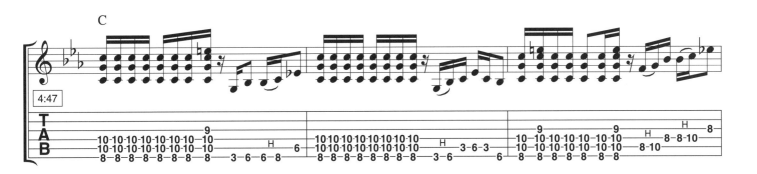

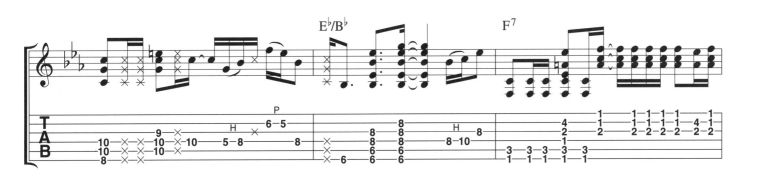

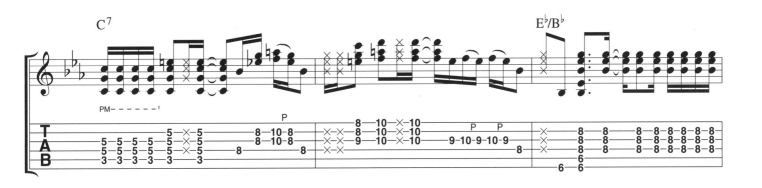

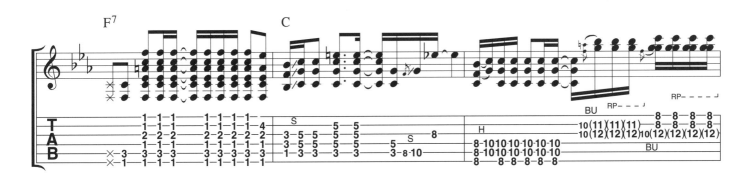

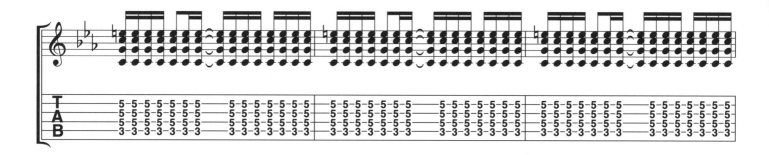

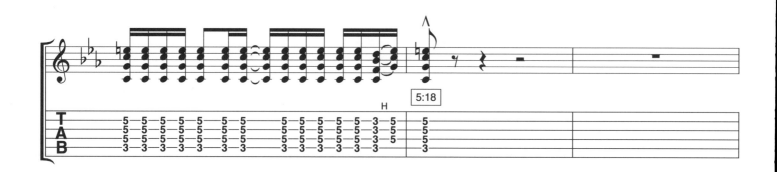

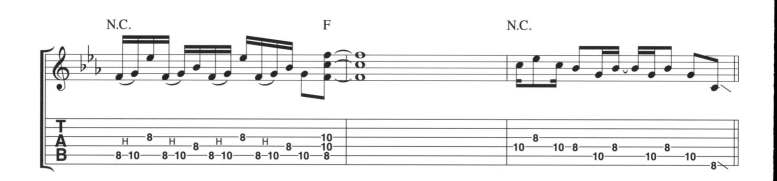

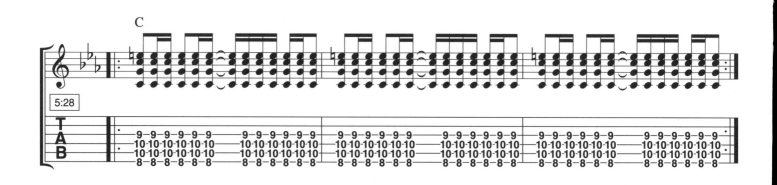

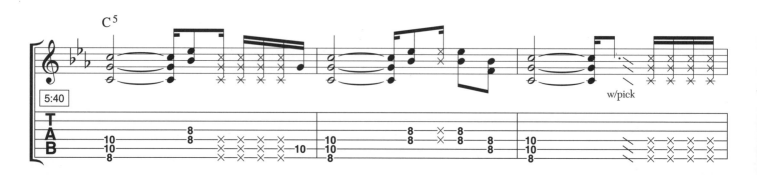

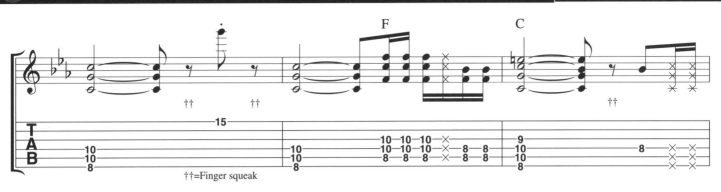

†† =Finger squeak

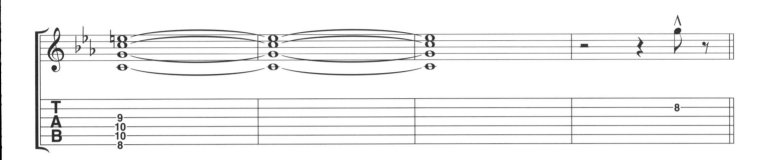

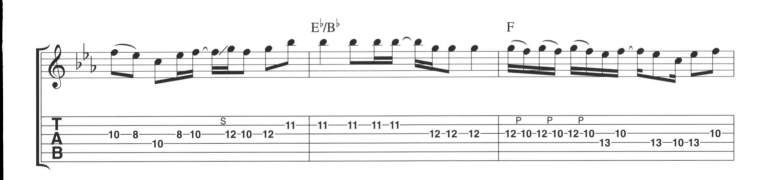

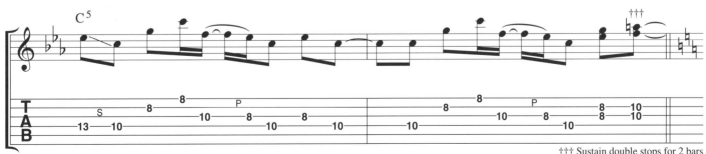

††† Sustain double stops for 2 bars

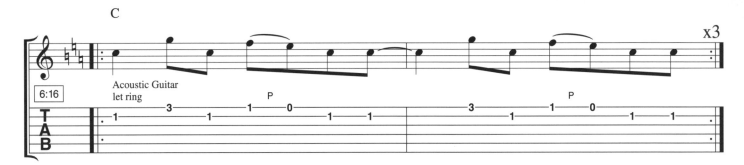

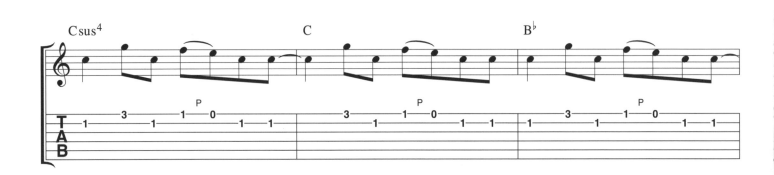

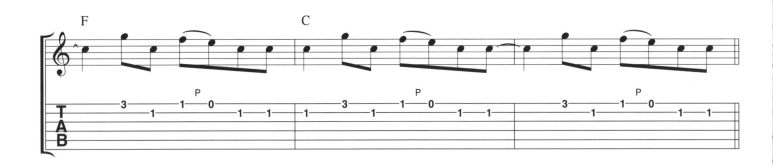

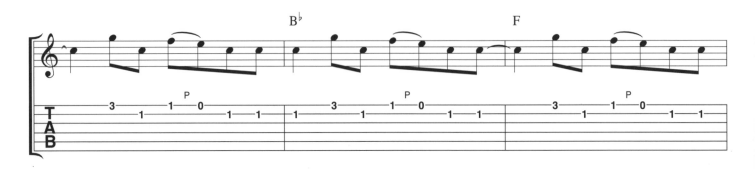

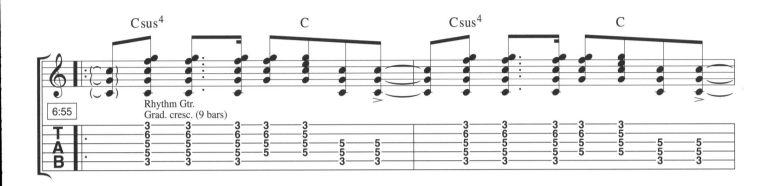

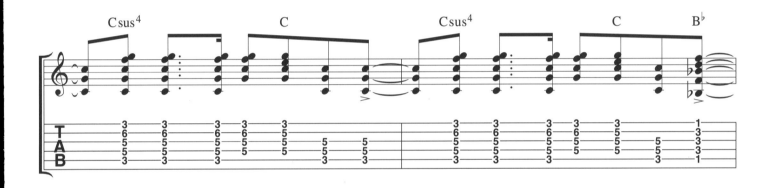

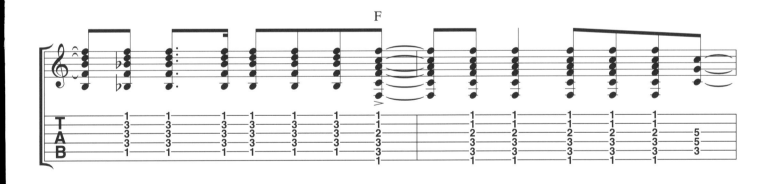

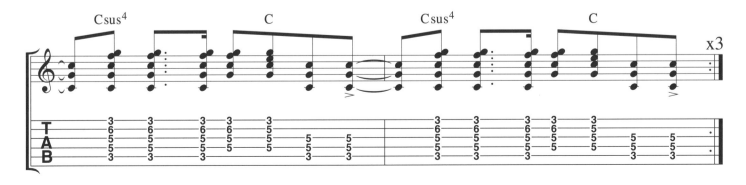

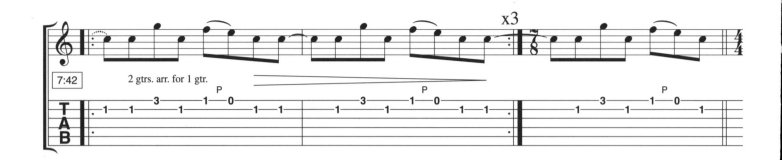

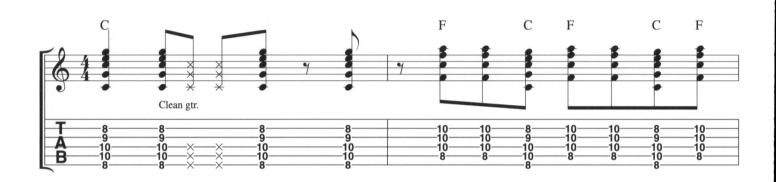

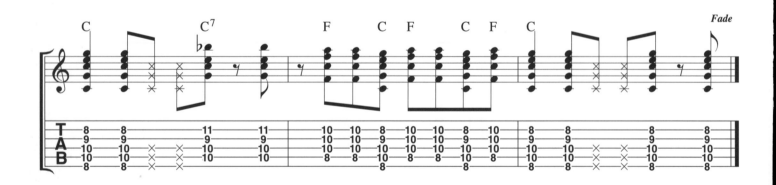

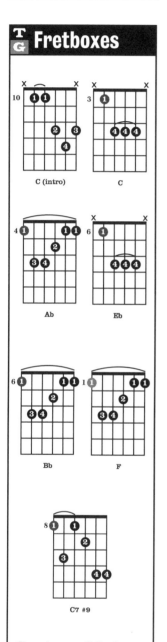
Hush

KULA SHAKER

This track has been recorded by two great bands, but 25 years apart! Here we transcribe Kula Shaker's funkier, up-tempo version.

Crispian Mills of Kula Shaker - "Hush, I'm taking a solo!"

THE other band in question, by the way, is Deep Purple. Their version of the original Joe South song was a typical rock anthem, making full use of the 'nah nah nah…' chorus. This 1997 version by 'Hindie' band Kula Shaker is a more up-tempo, energetic affair, from the funky 16s of the intro, through the stock-Hendrix C7#9 stabs, to the frenetic wah-wah solo.

GUITAR SOUND

Guitarist Crispian Mills uses a fairly standard setup, considering some of the wild sounds on Kula Shaker's more 'Eastern' sounding tracks. He's a confirmed Strat devotee; "I started on a Strat copy; then I went onto a Squier; then a Fender… the Strat's a versatile guitar and

you can put a lot of your character into it. I don't know anything about amps, but I've got a Fender Twin and a wah-wah and a multi-FX unit. I always use compression, overdrive and a lot of delay."

THE TRANSCRIPTION

Our version of *Hush* features all of the parts from the original, but as usual we've condensed the guitars into one single part that can be played solo – all other rhythm guitars are pre-recorded on the full band backing track. Incidentally, is it just me, or is the chord sequence from the chorus the same as Jimi Hendrix's *Hey Joe* transposed down a third? Kula Shaker have been called magpies before, but you be the judge! **TG**

Hush

Words & Music by Joe South

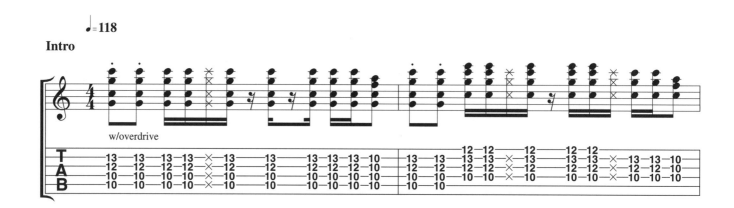

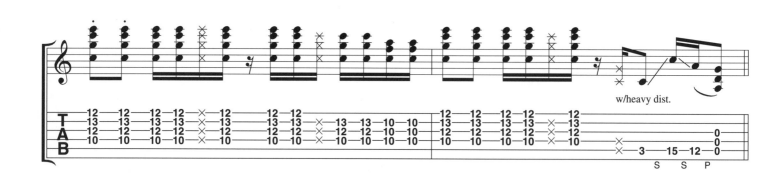

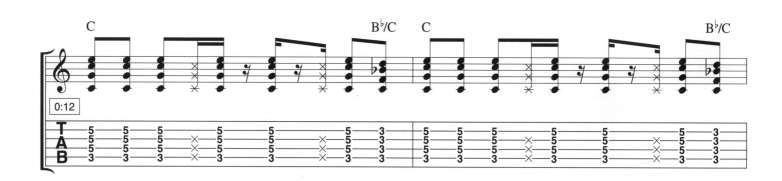

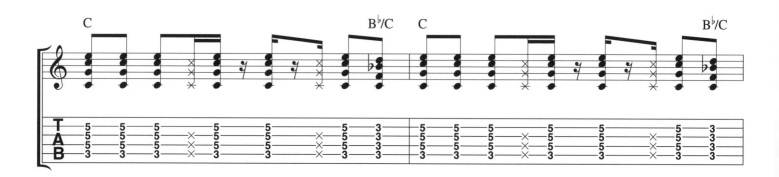

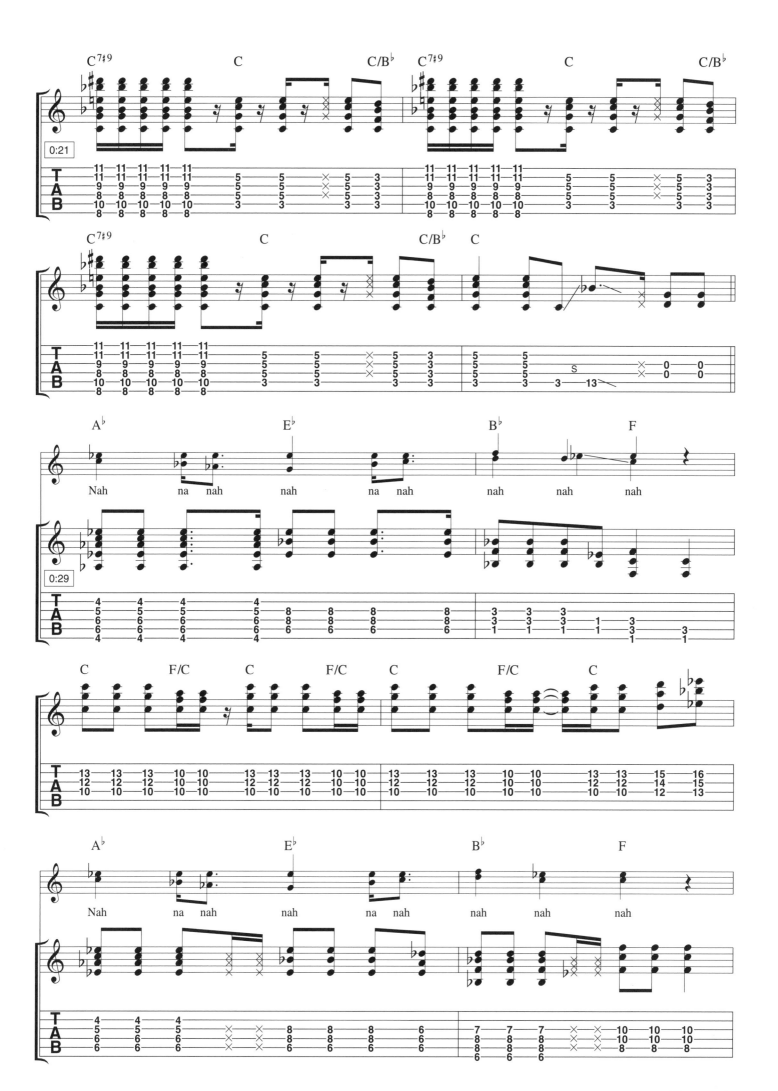

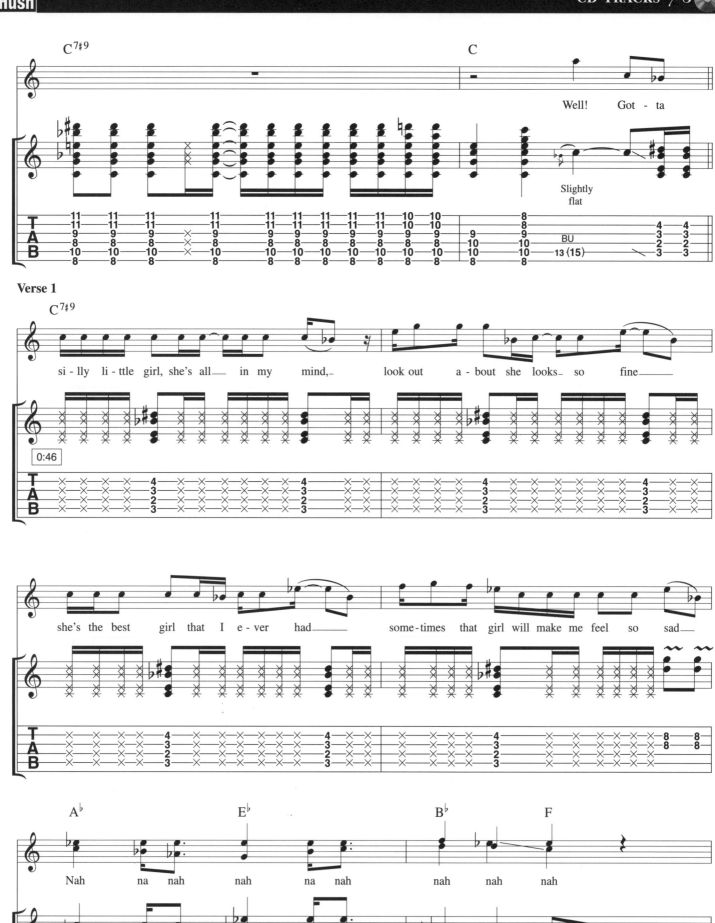

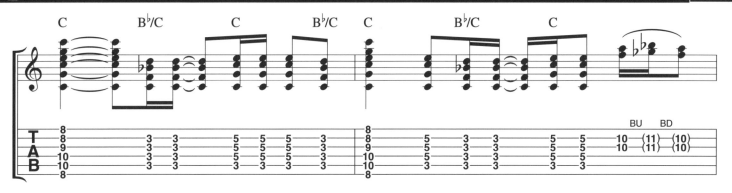

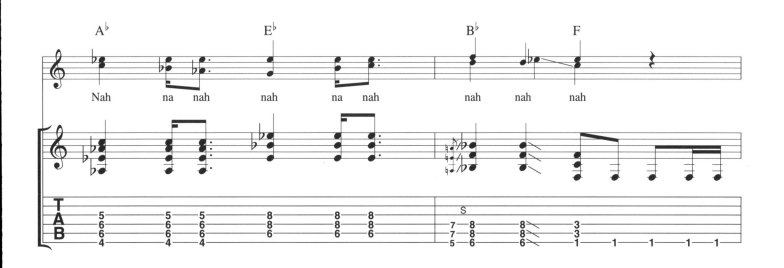

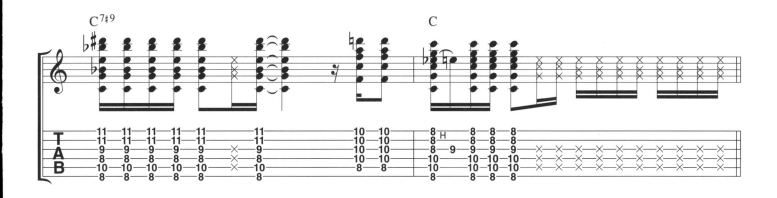

Chorus

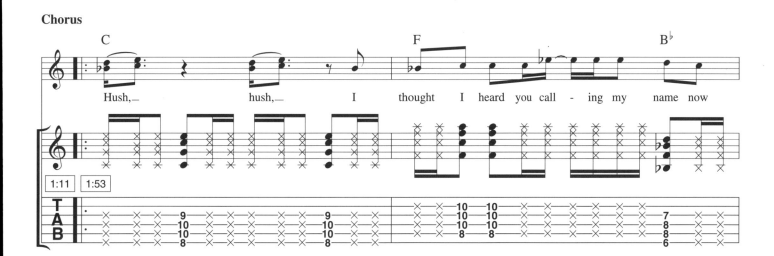

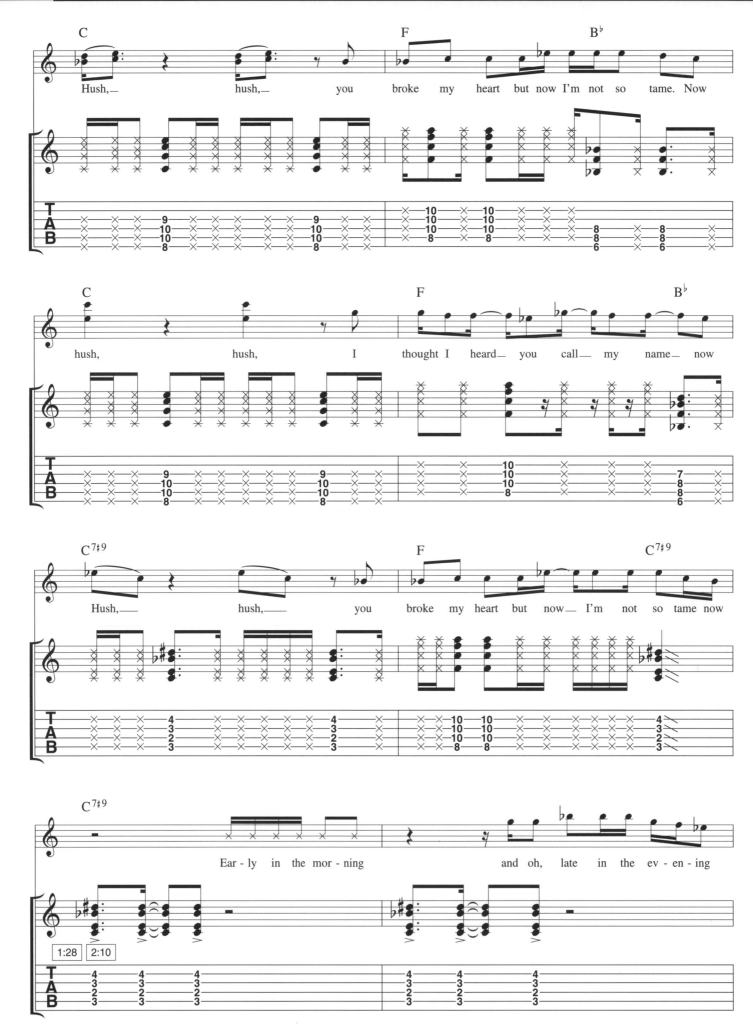

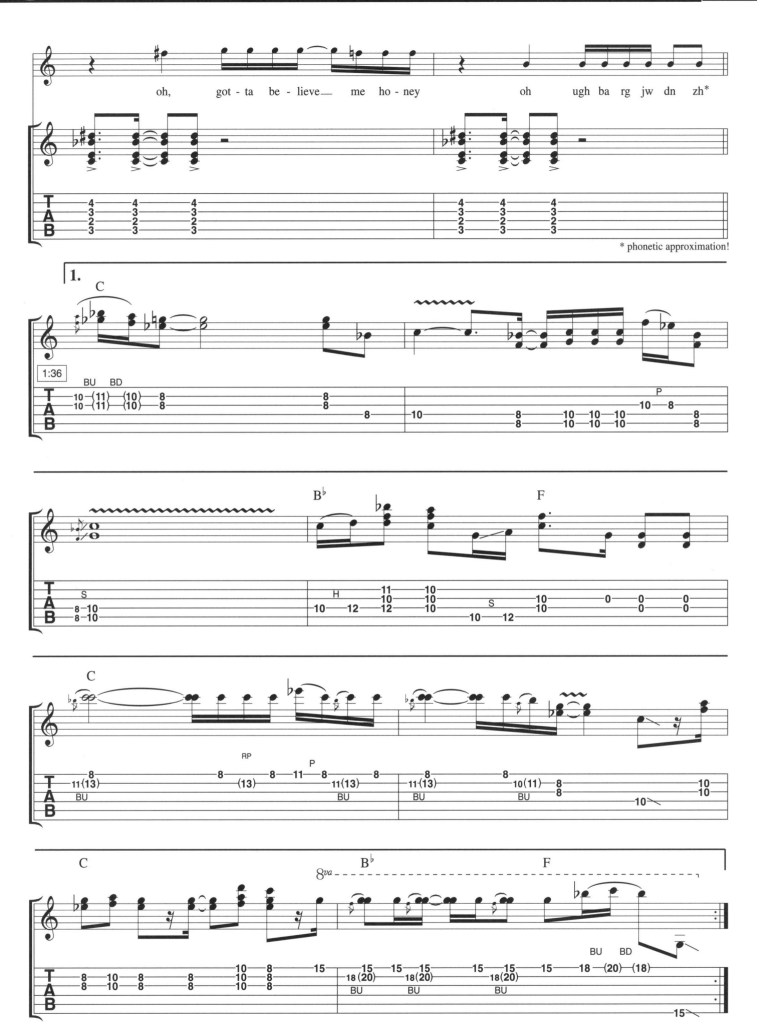

* phonetic approximation!

2.

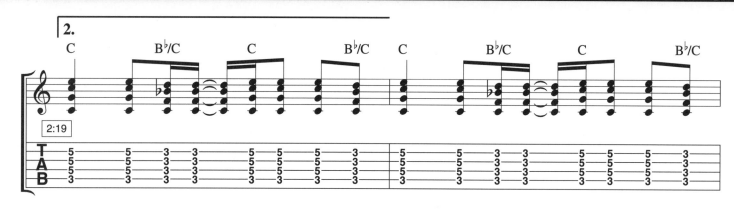

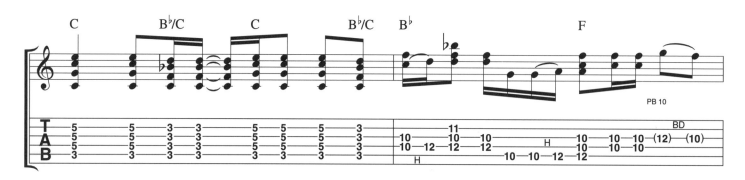

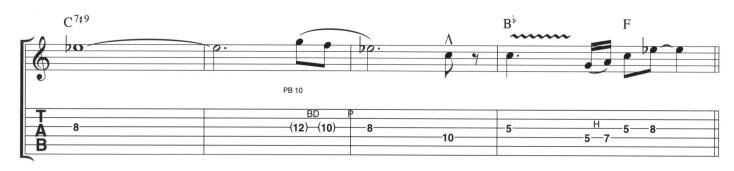

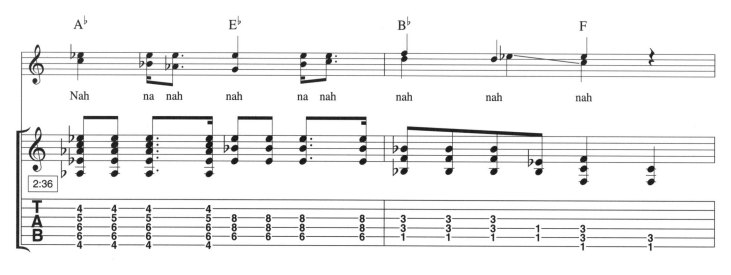

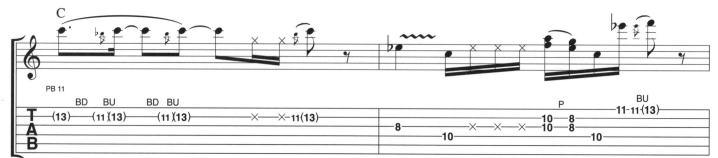

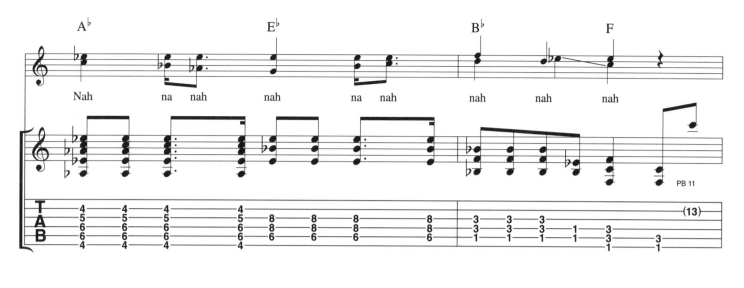

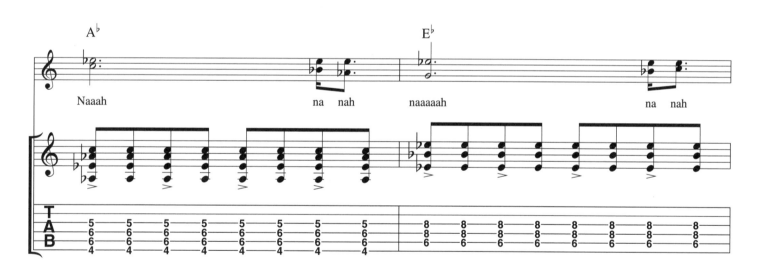

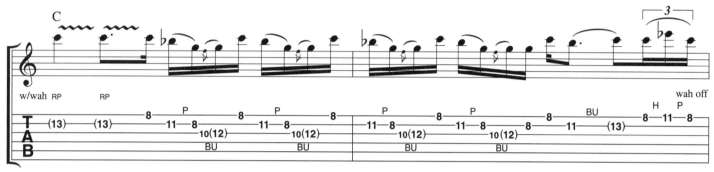

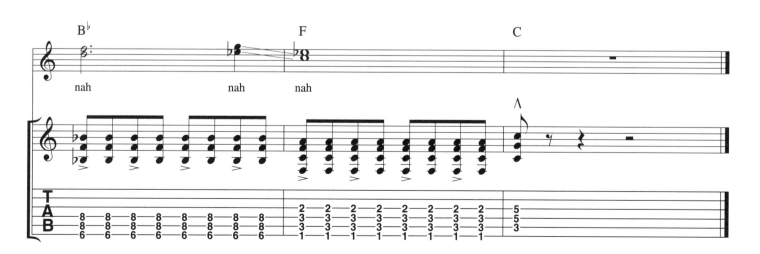

Walk This Way

AEROSMITH

This 1975 classic features one of the best-known riffs of all time. Originally a huge hit for Aerosmith it also helped to revive their fortunes with a little help from Run DMC...

The Joe Perry guitar sound

Most of the time, you'll find Joe Perry wielding one of his trademark Les Pauls - he favours either a 1960 model or his own Joe Perry signature axe. However, he has been known to use a '57 or 59 Strat for cleaner tones.

The 1986 version of Walk This Way used a fairly thick distortion; the original version transcribed here uses a more subtle amp overdrive. The guitar is double-tracked for most of the song, which can be simulated using a short delay (set your delay to between 50 and 80 milliseconds).

Make sure your pick-up selector is in the bridge position for that authentic Joe Perry sound.

Here's Joe himself to explain the genesis of this rock classic:

"I was into funky stuff, had played James Brown songs over the years, and at the time was listening to lots of the Meters from New Orleans, one of the best bands in the country, and I was asking 'Why don't we write our own songs that have that feel to them? Let's try to write something funky so we don't have to cover James Brown.' I came up with that riff, added it to another one I came up with while watching a Godzilla movie - one of my favourite compositional methods - and Steven wrote the lyrics on the stairwell of the Record Plant."

Joe Perry - The man behind many of rock's most classic guitar moments.

WALK *This Way* was a huge international hit, not once but twice. It first appeared on Aerosmith's third album *Toys In The Attic,* which for many is their best, and ten years later was recorded by early rappers Run DMC, with Tyler and Perry guesting on the single and appearing in the video.

With *Toys In The Attic* it became obvious that Aerosmith had a winning formula. Along with their contemporaries, Kiss, they wrote riff-driven grooves steeped in the staple diet of rock 'n' roll; sex, drugs and having a damn good time. Their low-down blues-rock became the soundtrack of '70s youth, it was stoned, hedonistic and utterly brilliant. Their sound was almost always driven by the rhythmic riffing of Perry's Les Paul, and despite surprisingly intricate harmonies and song structures, the songs never lost energy or spontaneity.

TECHNIQUE

Walk This Way is, of course, based on that great one-bar open E riff, but most players don't play it correctly when they first attempt it. It's tempting to play the first three notes as a double hammer-on in order to make the riff flow more smoothly, take another listen to the CD – every note is individually picked – which gives the track that 'lurching' rhythmic feel.

After the A5 passing chord comes the verse, which is played as a Status Quo-style C5-C6-C7 shape (see tab), but with each note picked rather than double-stopped. And just for the record, I *don't* know what those lyrics are about. Mind you, I had a very sheltered upbringing. **TG**

Walk This Way
Words & Music by Joe Perry & Steven Tyler

♩=110

Intro   **Main Riff**

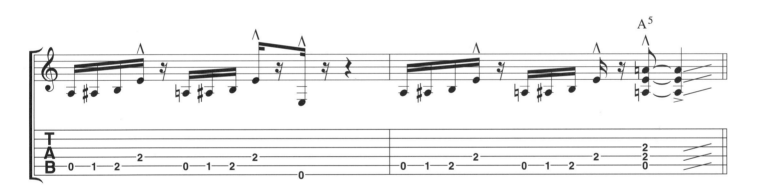

Verse

1. Back-stroke lov-er al-ways hid-ing 'neath the cov-ers 'til I talked to your Dad-dy, he say,— he said "Ya
3. School-girl swee-ty with a clas-sy kind-a sas-sy lit-tle skirts climb-in' way up the knee,— there was

ain't seen noth-in' 'til you're down on a muf-fin, then you're sure to be a chang-in' your ways." I met a
three young la-dies in the school gym lock-er when I no-ticed they was look-in' at me. I was a

cheer - lea - der, was a real young bleed-er, oh, the times I could rem-in-isce, 'cos the
high-school los-er, nev-er made it with a la-dy 'til the boys told me some-thin' I missed, then my

best things of lov-in' with her sis-ter and her cous-in on-ly star-ted with a lit-tle kiss, like this!
next-door neigh-bour with a daugh-ter had a fav-our so I gave her just a lit-tle kiss, like this!

Riff

N.C.

Gtr. 1

0:35
1:46

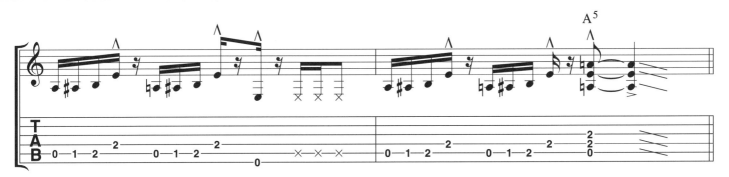

Verse

2. 4. See - saw swing-in' with the boys in the school and your feet are fly-in' up in the air,— sing-in'

Gtrs. 1 + 2

0:44

1:55

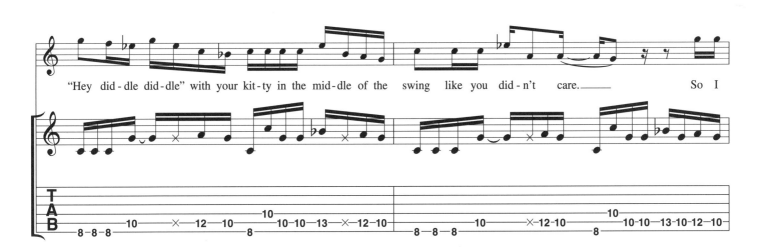

"Hey did - dle did - dle" with your kit-ty in the mid-dle of the swing like you did - n't care.— So I

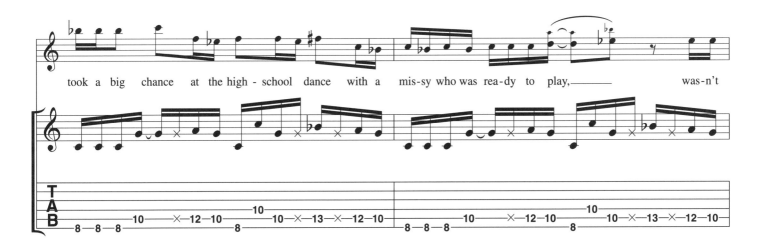

took a big chance at the high - school dance with a mis-sy who was rea-dy to play,— was-n't

Bridge

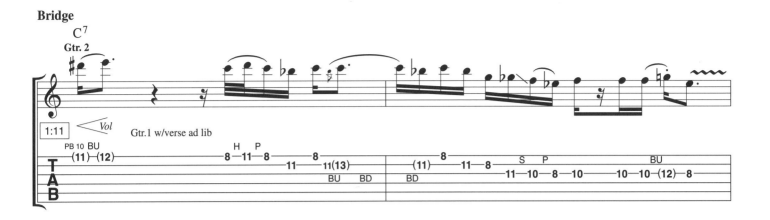

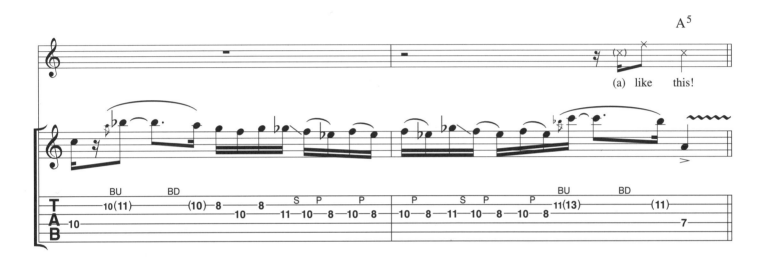

Riff

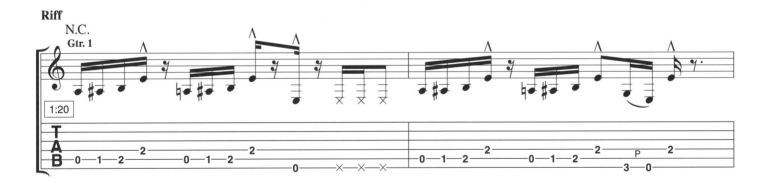

D.%. al Coda
with repeats

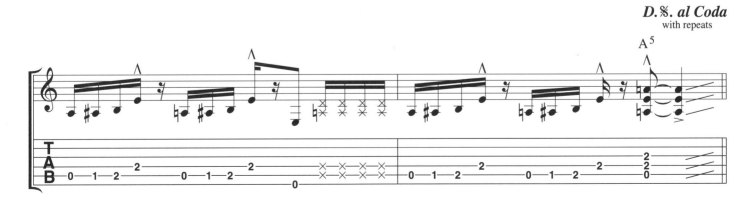

⊕ Coda

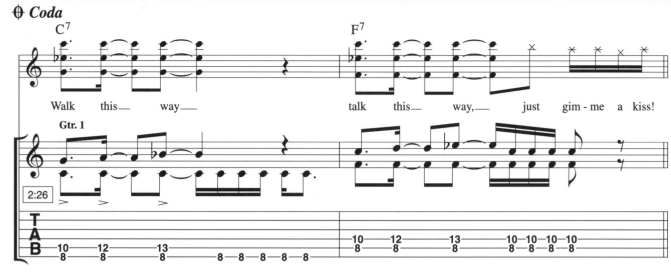

Walk this— way— talk this— way,— just gim-me a kiss!

Bridge

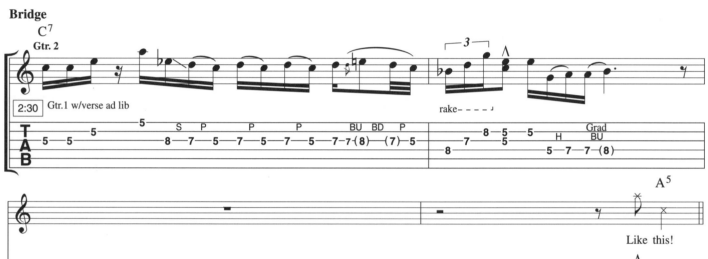

Gtr.1 w/verse ad lib

rake

Like this!

Outro (Gtr. Solo)

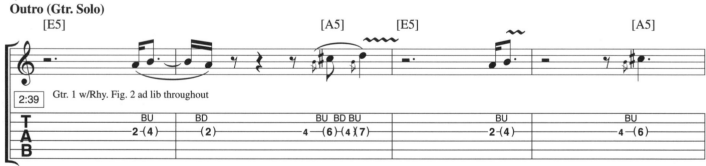

Gtr. 1 w/Rhy. Fig. 2 ad lib throughout

Rhy. Fig. 2

Gtr. 1

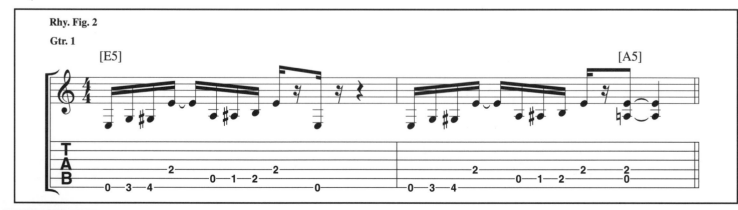

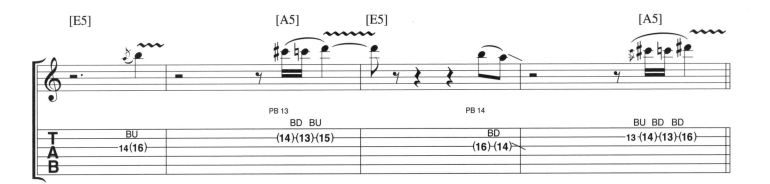

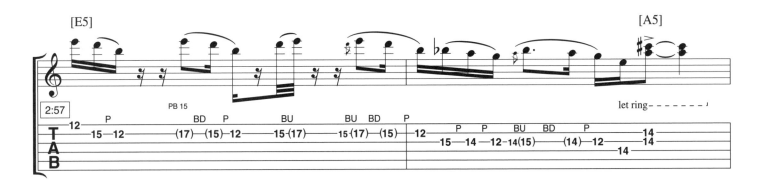

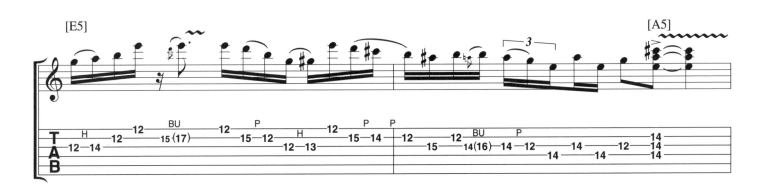

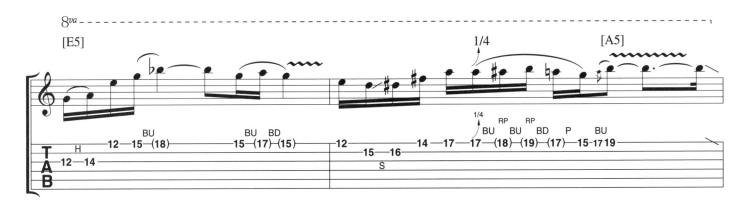

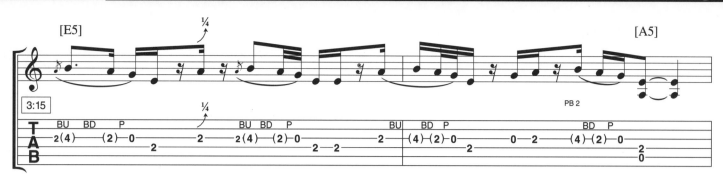

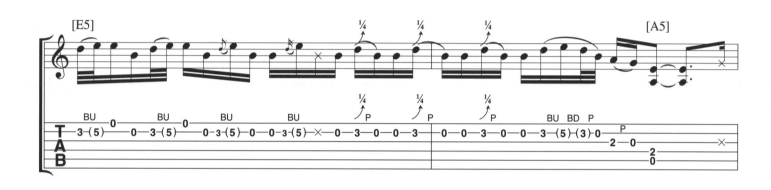

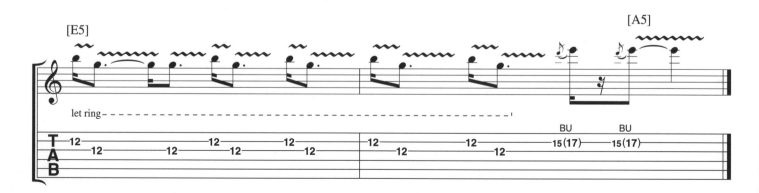

 On the CD

TRACK 11

Intro section

TRACK 12

First verse

TRACK 13

Verse 2/3, chorus

TRACK 14

Picked outro

TRACK 15

Backing track only

TG Tips

So you want to sound like the Edge?

Here's how to do it!

There is a great deal of guitar-shop discussion on the U2 sound, but here's how the man himself does it.

The basic tone is an old '60s Vox AC30, with the guitar compressed, and delay added – Edge favours rack delays including the TC Electronic 2290 and Korg SDD3000. To duplicate the sound for yourself, ideally you should try a Strat (use the middle or neck position), although you may need additional EQ to replicate that cutting tone exactly. Edge favours an MXR DynaComp compressor, but any type of heavy compression should fit the bill.

The guitar is only slightly overdriven, so keep the gain or drive setting in the lower areas. If you have a digital delay (either on a multi-FX or a pedal), set up a delay of about 350ms, with 20% feedback, and the delay signal almost as loud as the guitar (i.e. towards 100% level). The delay will create additional notes when you play along with the track.

Where The Streets Have No Name
U2

This 1987 single features Edge's characteristic echoing wall of guitars and still remains one of U2's crowning moments.

The Edge - An innovator, a great songwriter, one hell of a guitar player, and wearer of some very dodgy head gear!

THE Joshua Tree was U2's first number 1 album on both sides of the Atlantic, and *Where The Streets Have No Name* was the second of three singles released from it (*With Or Without You* and *I Still Haven't Found What I'm Looking For* being the others). The song features many of The Edge's musical trademarks, including rhythmic delays, muted chords and open drone notes.

STYLE

The track opens with picked palm-muted notes which work with a 'dotted' delay effect to create a sequencer-like cluster of semiquavers in 3/4 time. When the time changes to 4/4, Edge plays rapid up-and-down strokes, with the delay supplying additional chords in some of the gaps.

There are a couple of overdubbed parts that drop in and out at various parts - one plays sixteen-to-the-bar, using up and downstrokes with all six strings muted for a percussive effect, the other plays octave D notes in unison at the 7th fret, third string, and at the 10th fret, first string.

CHORDS

There are only five basic chords in the song – D, G, A, C and Bm, plus various extensions and suspensions. In fact, it's almost possible to play a D chord throughout because the bass supplies the root of the harmony. Much of the time, Edge only needs to play partial chords, because the combination of guitar tone, open notes, overdubs and delays creates a huge wall of sound, which has been U2's signature for many years. **TG**

Where The Streets Have No Name
Words & Music by U2

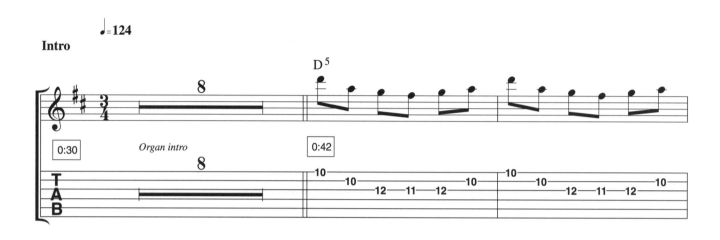

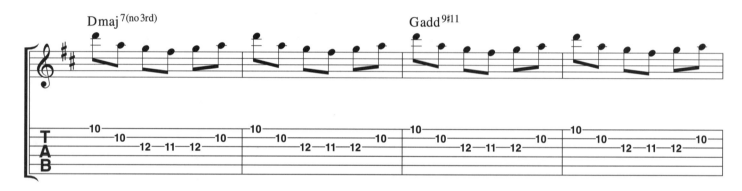

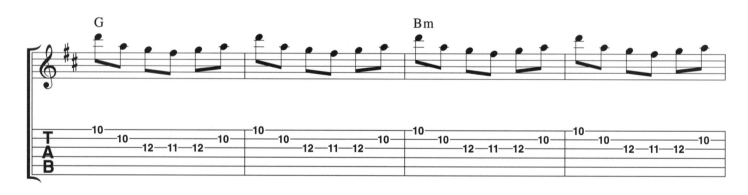

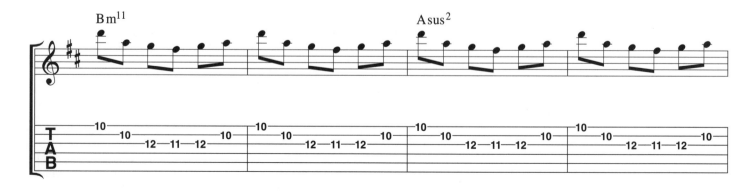

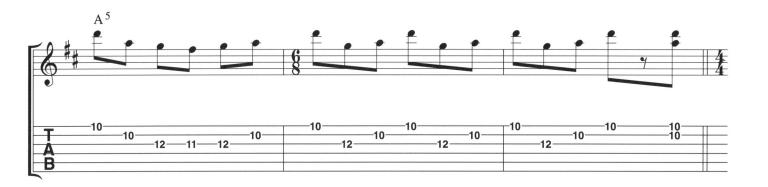

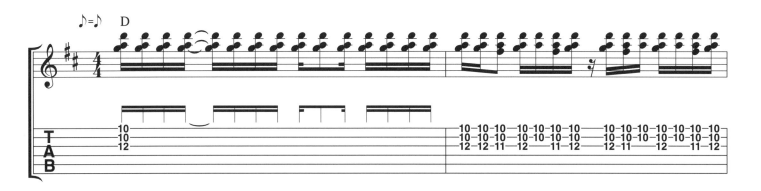

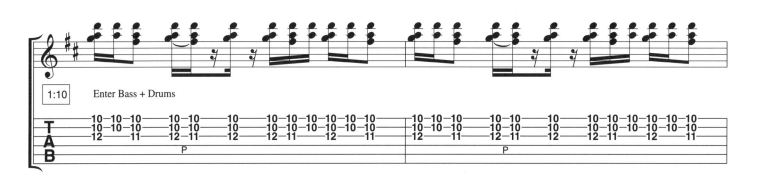

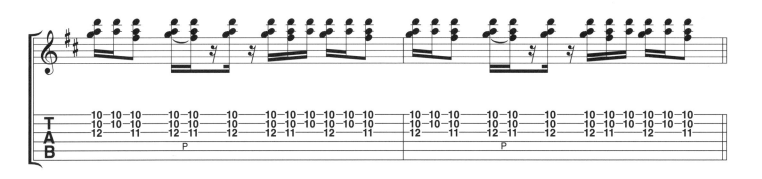

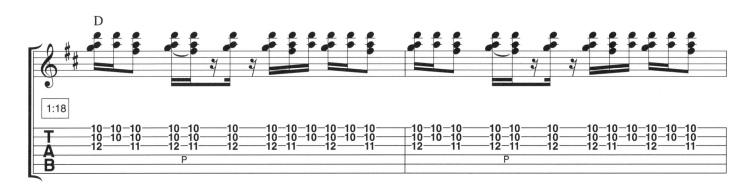

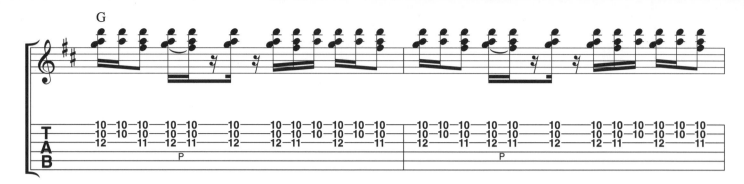

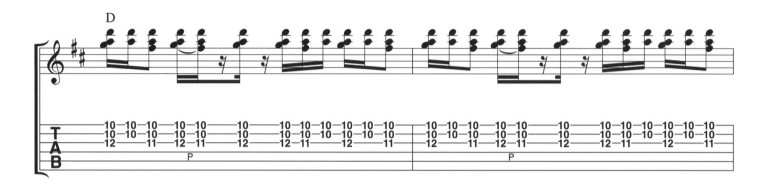

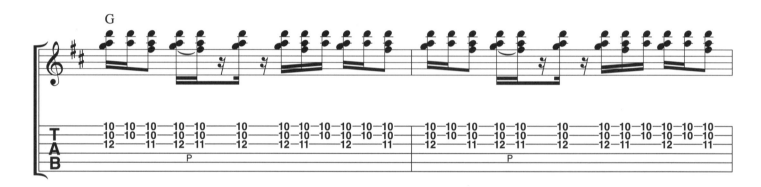

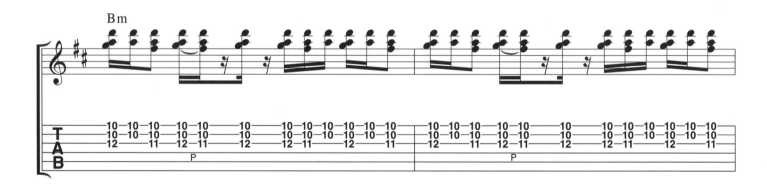

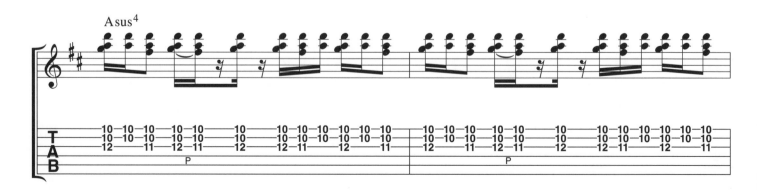

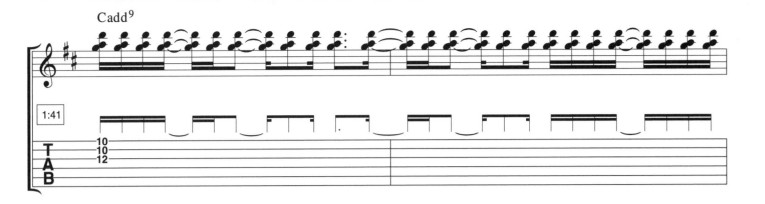

Cadd⁹

1:41

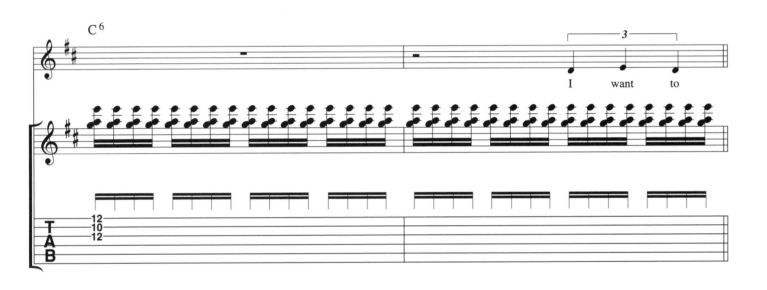

C⁶

I want to

Verse

D

run,

I____ want to hide.

1:48 Gtr 2 L.H. damping at 11th fret

Gtr 2 continues sim.

Gtr 1

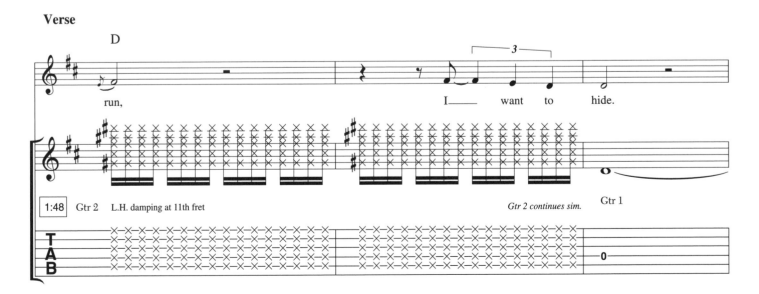

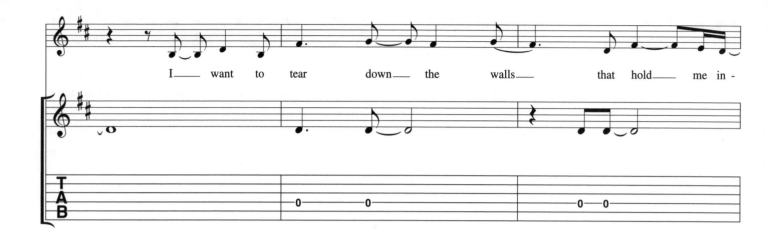

I___ want to tear down___ the walls___ that hold___ me in-

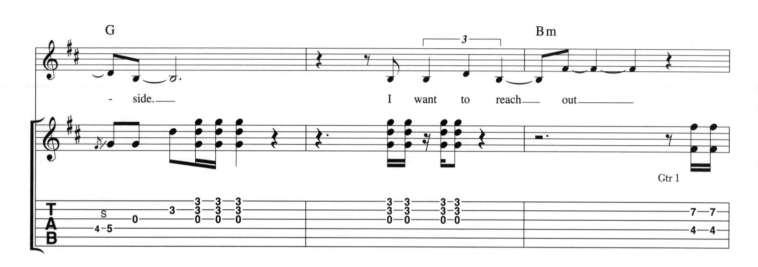

G

Bm

Gtr 1

-side.___ I want to reach___ out_____

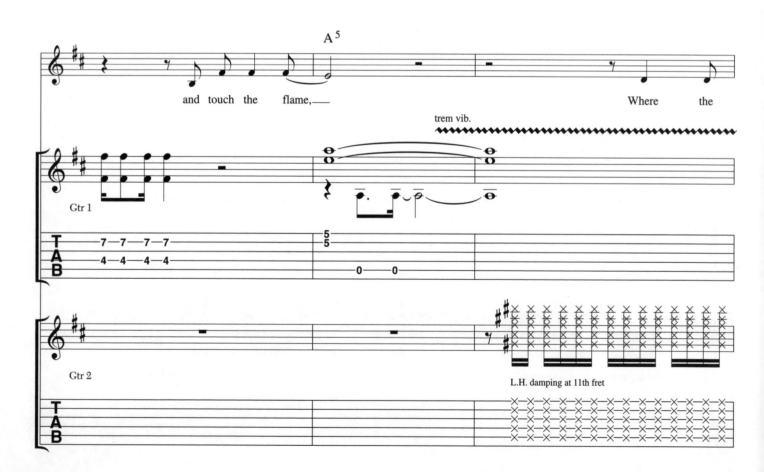

A⁵

and touch the flame,___ Where the

trem vib.

Gtr 1

Gtr 2

L.H. damping at 11th fret

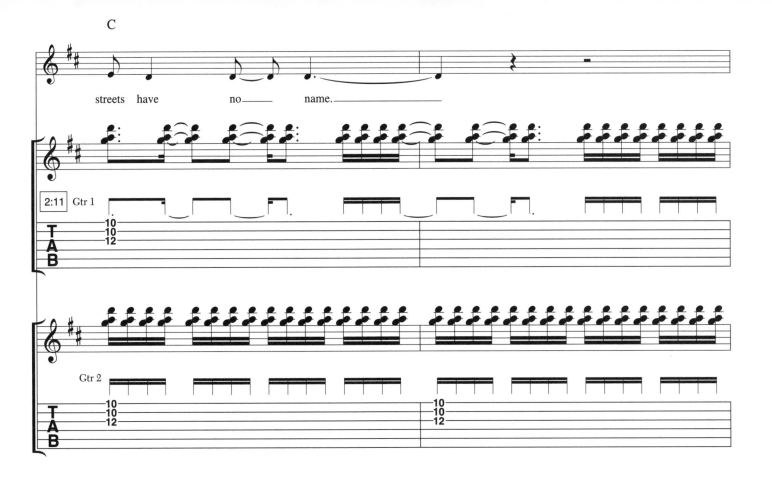

streets have no name.

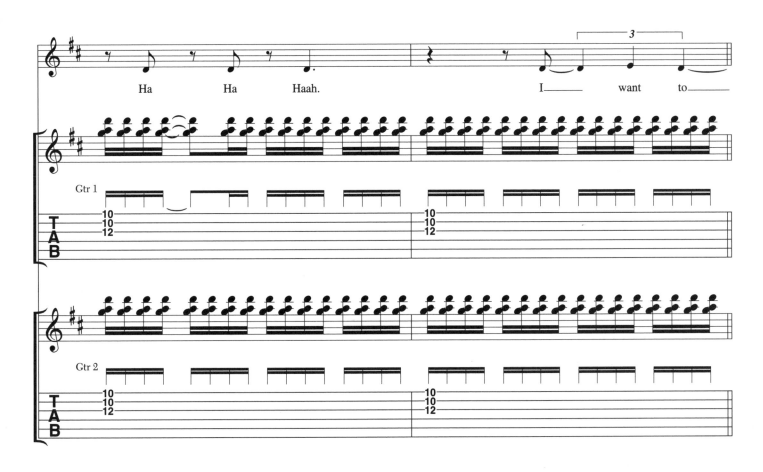

Ha Ha Haah.

I want to

Verse

D

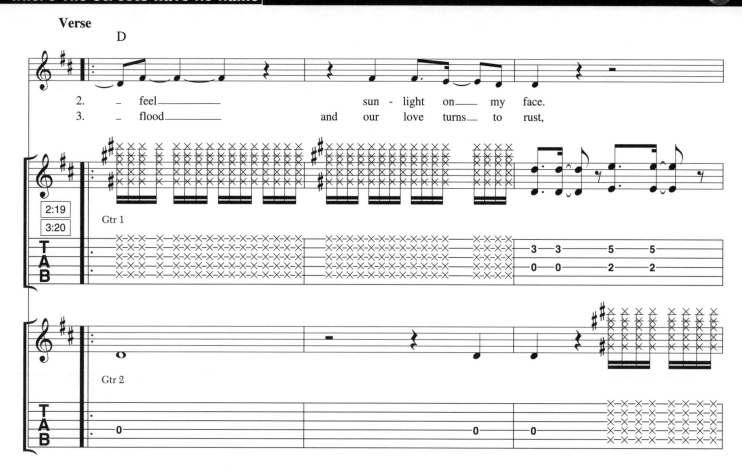

2. _ feel_____ sun - light on___ my face.
3. _ flood_____ and our love turns___ to rust,

Gtr 1

2:19
3:20

Gtr 2

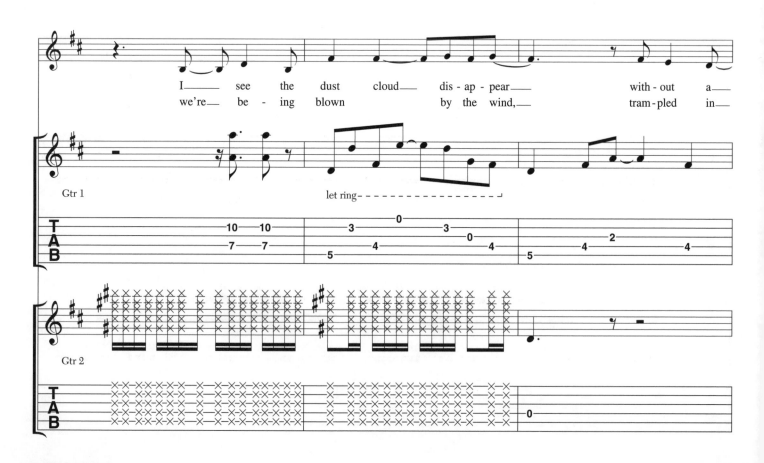

I_____ see the dust cloud___ dis-ap-pear___ with-out a_
we're___ be - ing blown by the wind,___ tram-pled in___

Gtr 1

let ring - - - - - - - - - - - - - - - -

Gtr 2

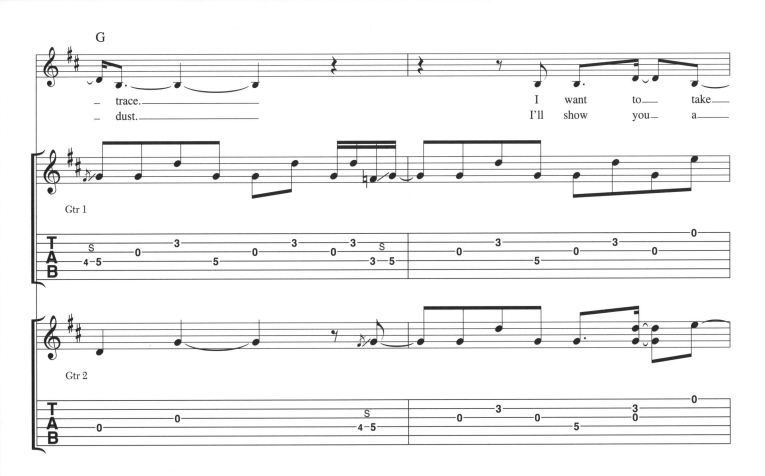

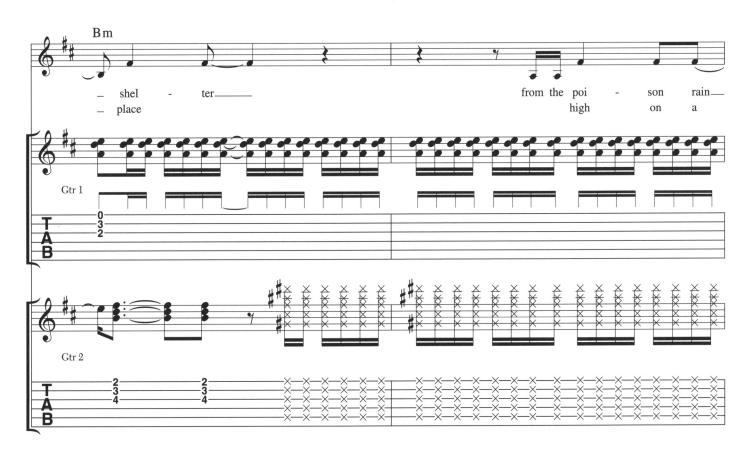

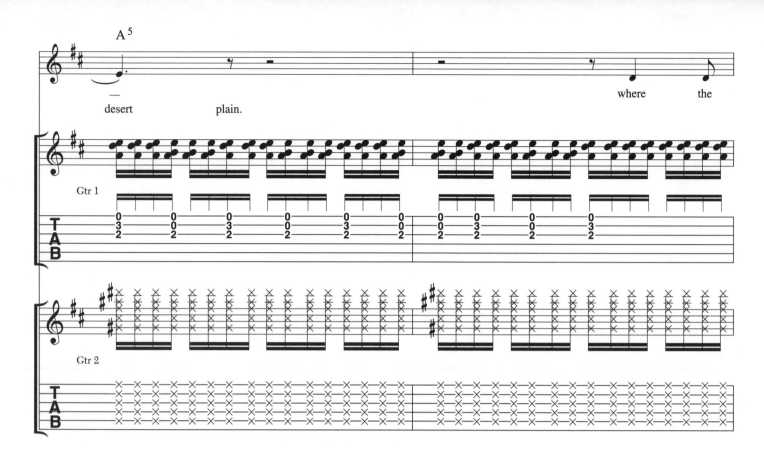

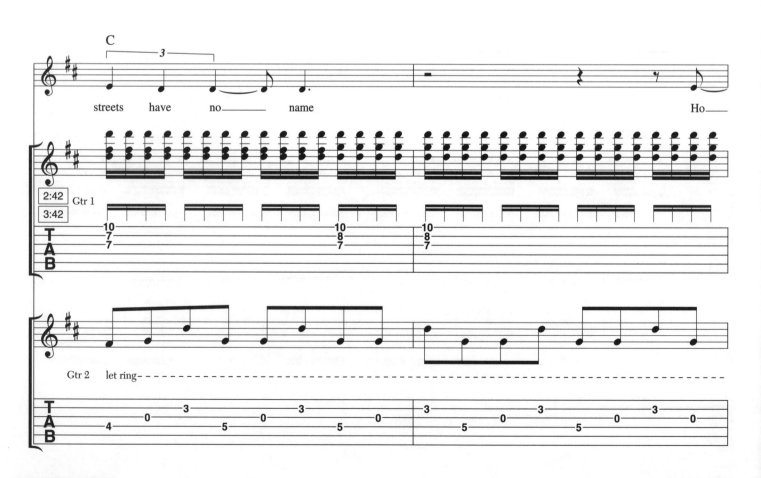

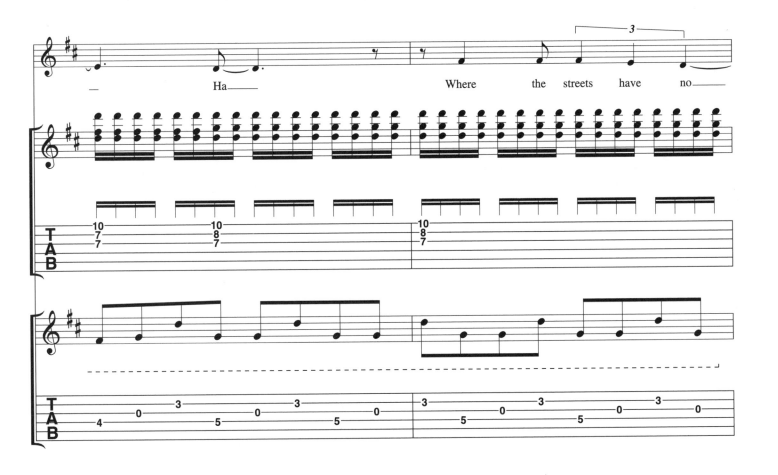

Ha— Where the streets have no—

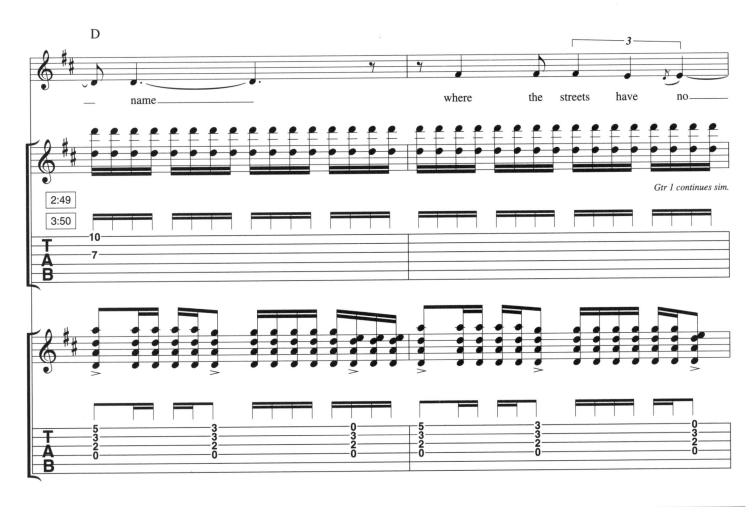

D

name— where the streets have no—

2:49

3:50

Gtr 1 continues sim.

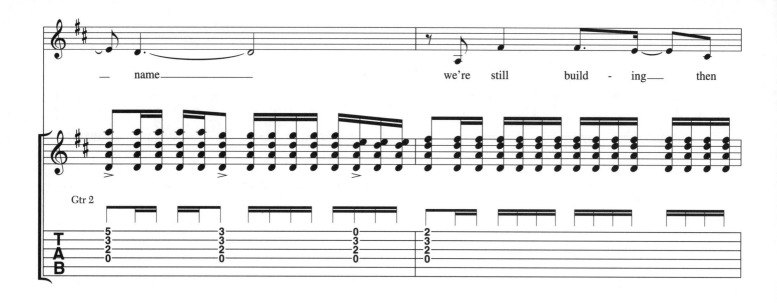

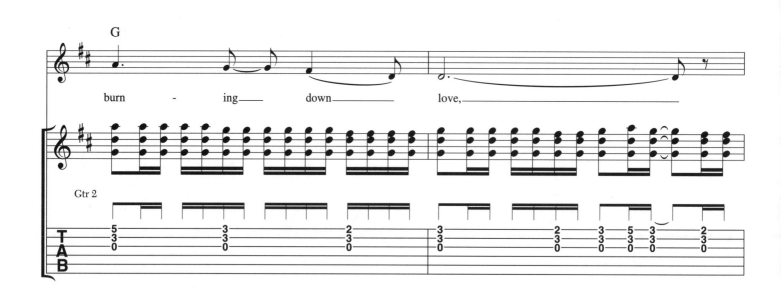

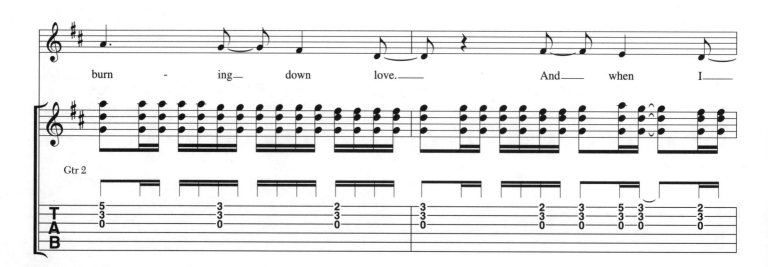

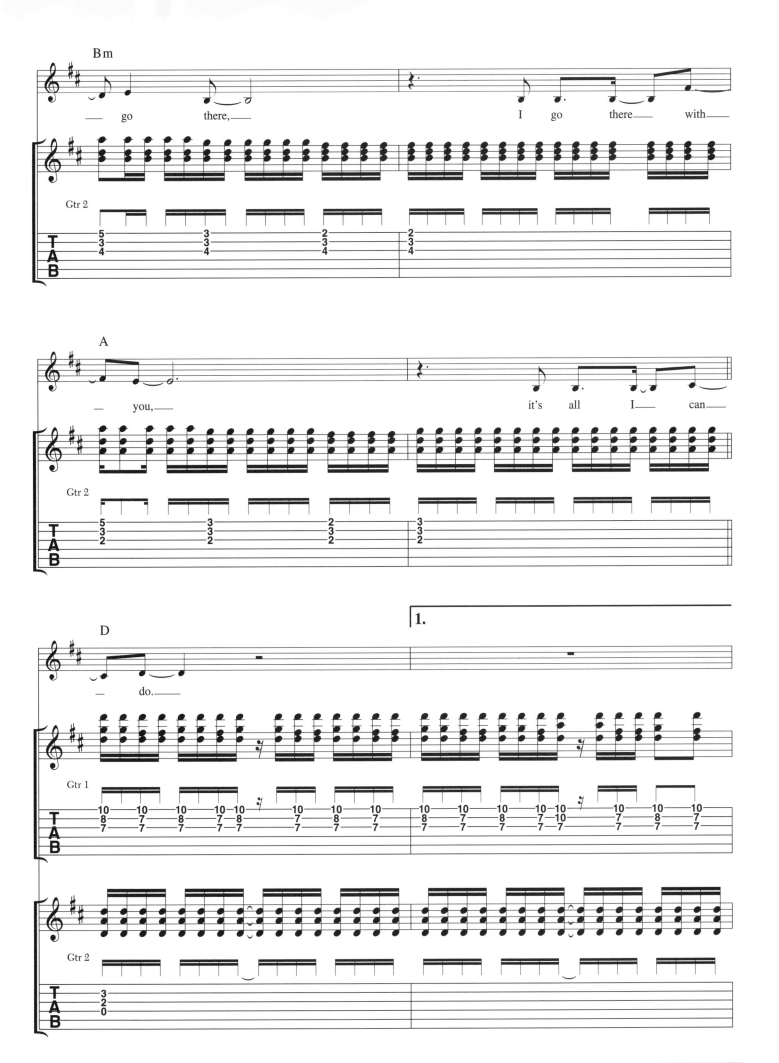

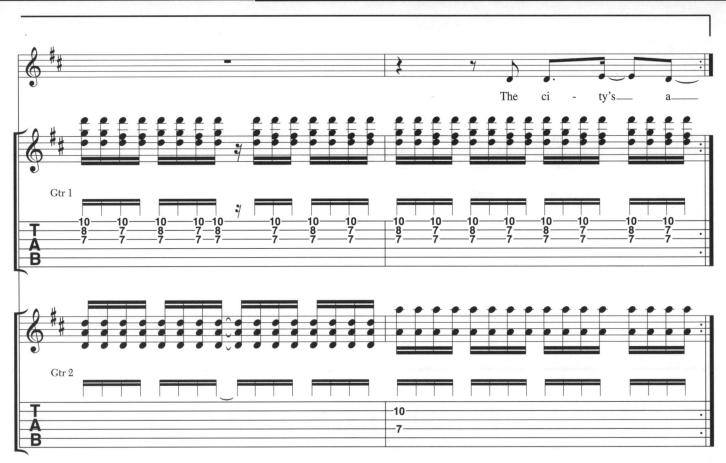

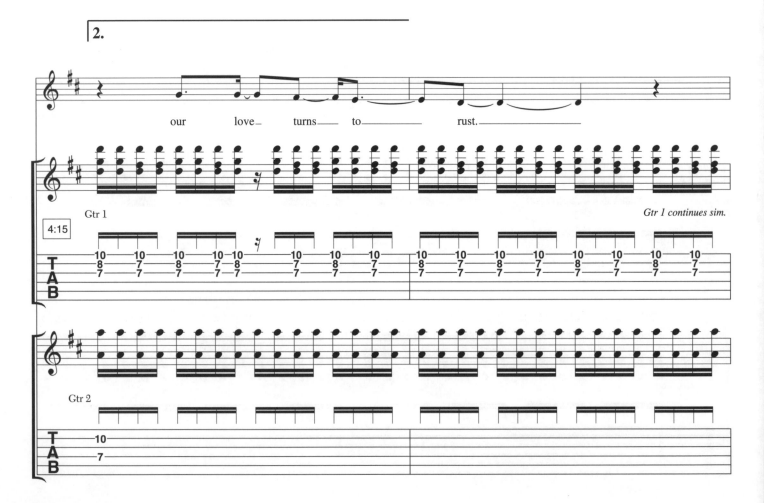

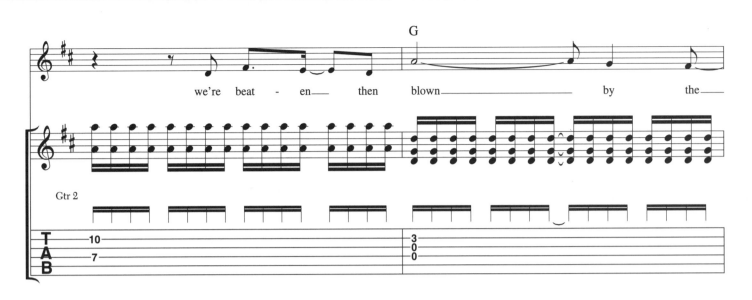

we're beat - en— then blown——————— by the——

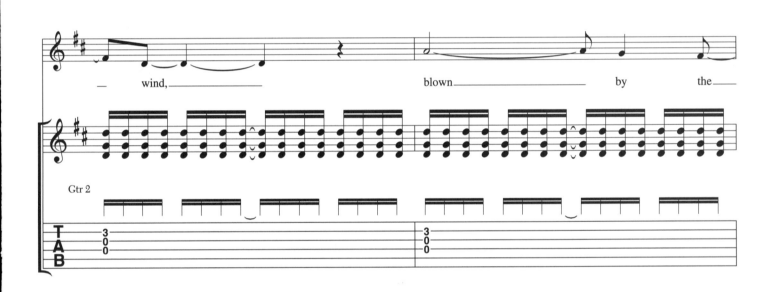

— wind,——————— blown———————— by the——

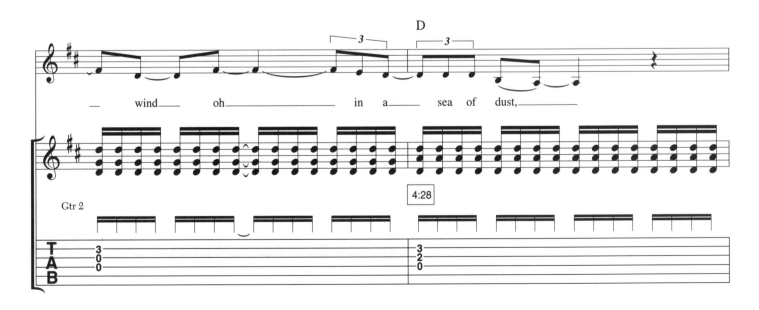

— wind— oh——————— in a— sea of dust,———————

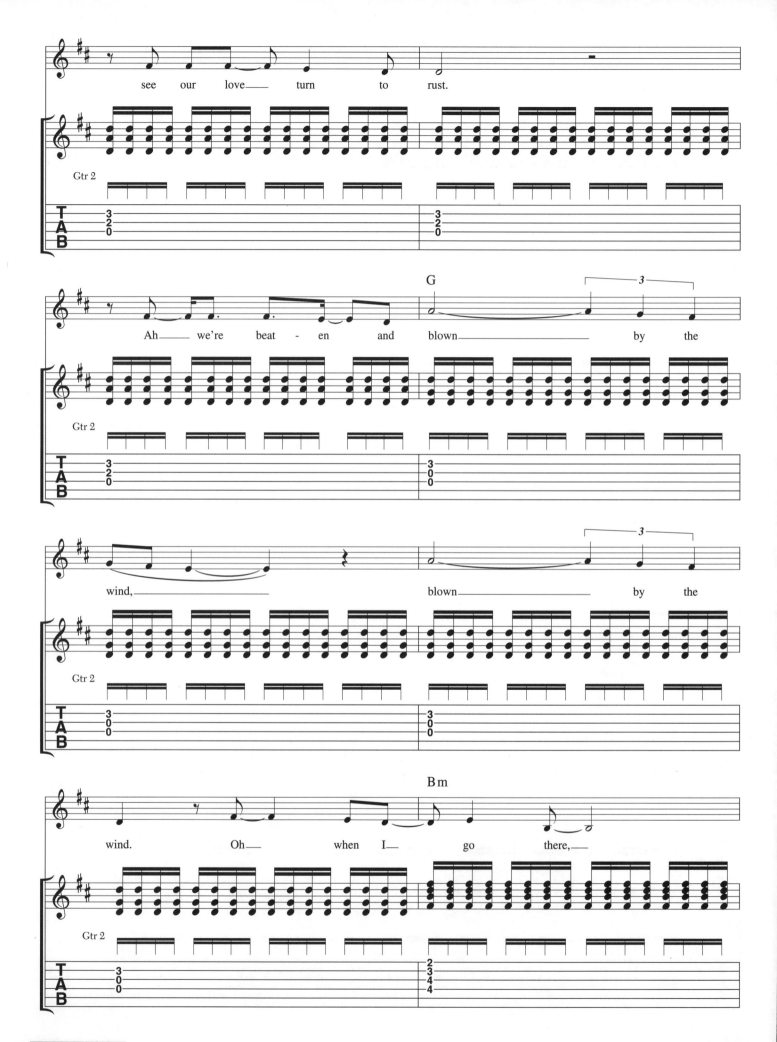

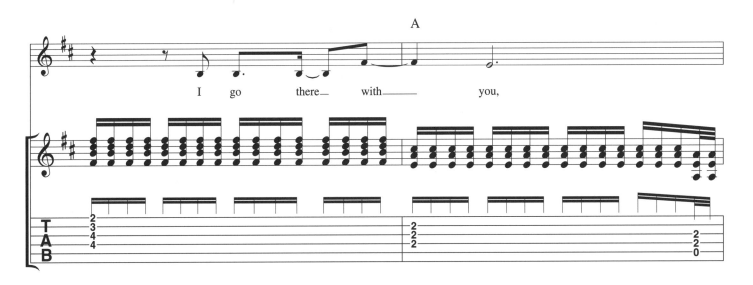

I go there— with—————— you,

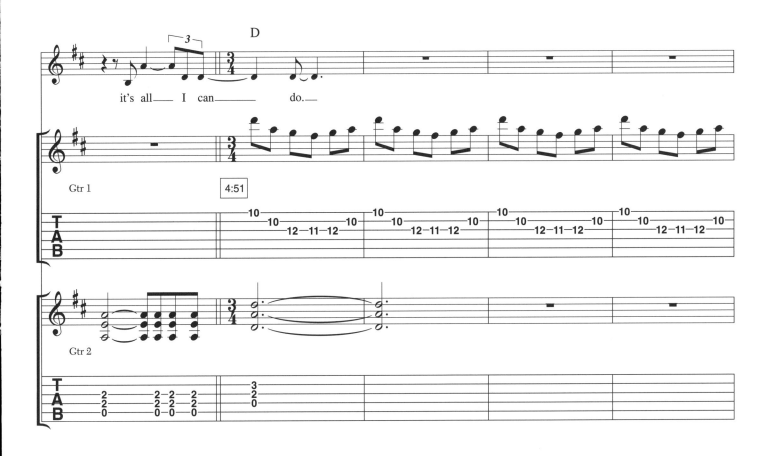

it's all— I can———— do.—

Gtr 1

4:51

Gtr 2

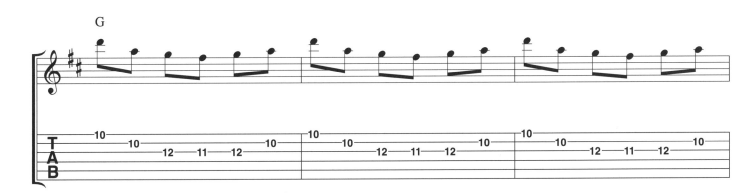

Gtr 1

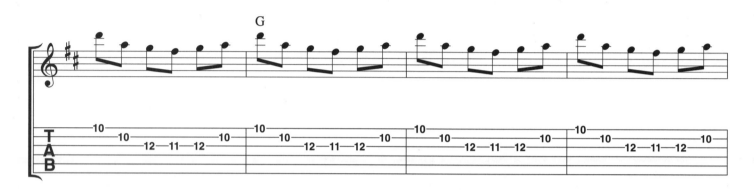

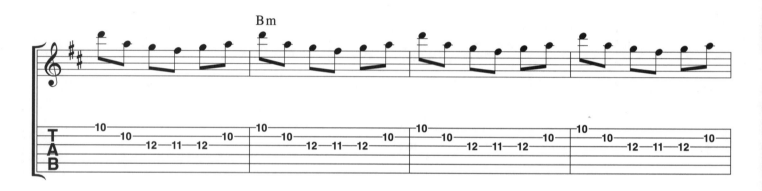

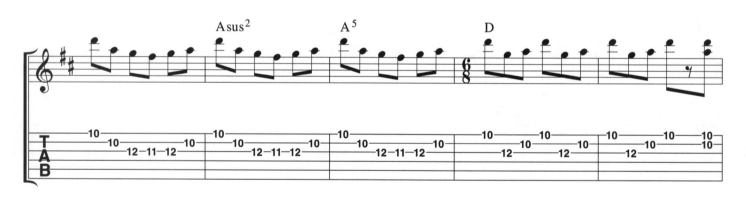

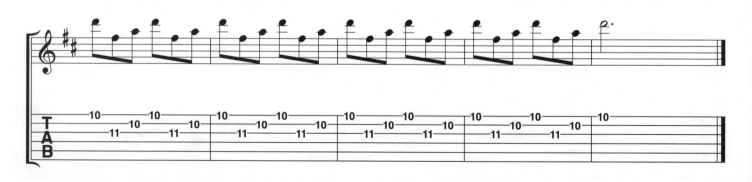

NOTATION AND TABLATURE

The Total Guitar tab and notation system covers all the commonly used guitar techniques, and is designed to be as easy to read as possible. The examples shown here explain what it all means...

TREBLE CLEF AND TABLATURE EXAMPLE

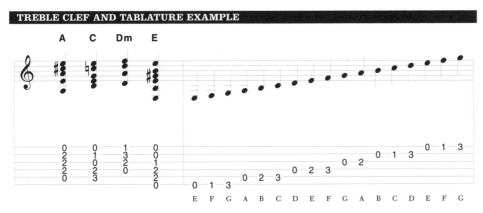

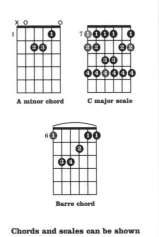

A minor chord   C major scale

Barre chord

Chords and scales can be shown in a fretbox, like this. Grey circles show root notes of the key, Black circles show other scale tones, and numbers give the fingering. Strings marked 'O' are open notes, and those marked 'X' should not be played.

The treble clef (top) shows the musical pitches of the notes you play. The lines (bottom) correspond to the strings of the guitar; the bass E (sixth) string is shown at the bottom. The numbers show the position where you fret the note – a zero means play the open string. This example shows four simple chords represented in tab, plus some of the note names available on the first few frets.

BEND UP/DOWN
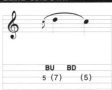

Fret the start note (here, the 5th fret) and bend up to the pitch of the bracketed note, before releasing again.

REPICK
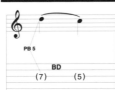

Bend up to the pitch shown in brackets, then pick the note again while holding the bent note at the pitch shown.

PRE-BEND

Bend the note up (from the 5th fret) to the pitch of the 7th fret note before you pick it, then pick and release.

HAMMER-ON
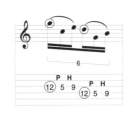

Pick the note at the fifth fret, then sound the seventh fret using the fretboard hand without repicking the note.

PULL-OFF
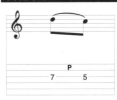

Fret the note at the seventh fret and also the fifth with another finger, then pull the finger off to sound the note.

SLIDE (GLISSANDO)
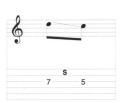

Pick the 7th fret note, then slide the finger down to the 5th without repicking.

FRETBOARD MUTES
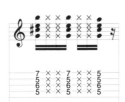

Notes marked with an X should be damped using the fingers of the fretting hand.

PALM MUTES
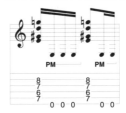

Mute by resting the fleshy part of the picking hand on the strings near the bridge.

RIGHT-HAND TAPPING
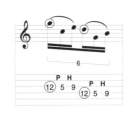

Tap onto the the circled 12th fret notes using one finger of the picking hand.

LEFT-HAND TAPPING

Sound the notes marked with a square with the fretting hand.

NATURAL HARMONICS

Touch the string over the fret indicated, pick it firmly, and remove the picking hand.

PINCHED HARMONICS

Fret where shown, but dig into the string with the side of the thumb as you pick.

VIBRATO

Wobble the note with the fretting hand, usually with an up-and-down motion.

WHAMMY BAR DIVE
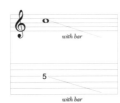

Pick the note, then depress the whammy bar so that the pitch of the note descends.

WHAMMY BAR BENDS
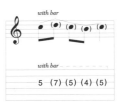

Using the bar, bend the note up or down to the pitches indicated in the notation.

A Design For Life (*Manic Street Preachers*)
(Bradfield/Moore/Wire) Sony/ATV Music Publishing (UK) Ltd.

1. Full performance
2. Backing track only

Don't Look Back In Anger (*Oasis*)
(Gallagher) Oasis Music/Creation Songs Ltd/Sony/ATV Music Publishing (UK) Ltd.

3. Full performance
4. Backing track only

I Am The Resurrection (*The Stone Roses*)
(Squire/Brown) Zomba Music Publishers Ltd

5. Full performance
6. Backing track only

Hush (*Kula Shaker*)
(South) BMG Music Publishing Ltd.

7. Full performance
8. Backing track only

Walk This Way (*Aerosmith*)
(Perry/Tyler) Sony/ATV Music Publishing (UK) Ltd.

9. Full performance
10. Backing track only

Where The Streets Have No Name (*U2*)
(U2) Blue Mountain Music Ltd.

11. Intro section
12. First verse
13. Verse 2/3, chorus
14. Picked outro
15. Backing track only

MCPS

Enhanced CD: The audio on the Enhanced CD can be played on either your Hi-fi or multimedia PC. If you are on the Internet and want to browse the World's largest selections of sheet music, simply place the CD in your CD-Rom drive and follow the on-screen instructions.